Rev. Gary Davis/Blues Guitar

by Stefan Grossman

Oak Publications, New York

Music Sales Limited, London

"...I met Gary in 1931 in Durham at the White House—that's the place they have tobacco sales. One night me and a friend picked him up and carried him out to the country. Gary was the fastest man I heard. I never heard a man pick a string like Gary.

You might find somebody make some of his chords, but you don't find anybody pick a string like Gary. Fuller used to say, 'All of us boys can play, Willy, but Gary is our Daddy!'

He called him the Daddy because he was the Daddy of the guitar players, not because he was older than us."

from an interview with Willy Trice

PHOTOGRAPHS

Georges Chatelain: Pages 25, 36, 65, 87, and 99
David Gahr: Page 76
Stefan Grossman: Pages 33, 45, 47, 62, and 71
Linda Fitzgerald Moore: Page 41
Brian Shuel: Page 93
Julie Snow: Page 69
R. Tilling: Page 22

Book design by Jean Hammons and Christine Czarny

© Oak Publications 1974
A Division of Embassy Music Corporation
24 East 22nd Street, New York, NY 10010 USA

Music Sales Limited,
8/9 Frith Street, London W1V 5TZ England

Music Sales (Pty.) Limited
120 Rothschild Street, Rosebery, Sydney, NSW 2018, Australia

International Standard Book Number 0-8256-0152-5
Library of Congress Catalogue Card Number 74-76793

Contents

Introduction to the Country Blues Guitar Series

"Objective music is all based on 'inner octaves'. And it can obtain not only definite psychological results but definite physical results. There can be such music as would freeze water. There can be such music as would kill a man instantaneously. The Biblical legend of the destruction of the walls of Jericho by music is precisely a legend of objective music. Plain music, no matter of what kind, will not destroy walls, but objective music indeed can do so. And not only can it destroy but it can also build up. In the legend of Orpheus there are hints of objective music, for Orpheus used to impart knowledge by music. Snake charmers' music in the East is an approach to objective music, of course very primitive. Very often it is simply one note which is long drawn out, rising and falling only very little; but in this single note 'inner octaves' are going on all the time and melodies of 'inner octaves' which are inaudible to the ears but felt by the emotional center. And the snake hears this music or, more strictly speaking, he feels it, and obeys it. The same music, only a little more complicated, and men would obey it."

From the teachings of G. I. Gurdieff

I remember seeing Son House at the Gaslight Cafe in New York City. He had just been rediscovered and was still quite nervous to play before people. He slowly rambled up to the stage and took a seat. The lights were bright and made it almost impossible for him to see the audience. Next the steel guitar was handed to him and he fumbled to get a brass piece of tubing from his vest pocket. The Cafe was full of noise and excitement. There was little recognition of Son's being on stage. Then to quiet the place an announcement was made introducing the "legendary bluesman from the Mississippi delta." Still noise, as most of the audience were very unfamiliar with delta music or Son House.

Then the amazing part of the night occurred. Son slid the slide down the fingerboard of the guitar. The sound cried out. Everyone stood and looked. Next Son started his singing moan. His eyes rolled, arms shook, sweat quickly rolled down his forehead. Everyone remained standing amazed at the sound. The song ended and in the speechless faces of everyone a wave of applause emerged. Son played four more songs. The blues brought tears to people who had never been exposed to this type of sound. Those familiar with Son and his music cried for the joy of seeing him perform and from the wailing sounds of the guitar.

Music is quite a powerful tool. Words of explanation can never express the impact of a musical experience. I am going to attempt to teach the music of some great guitar bluesmen. It is not going to be isolated and picked apart but instead presented with its historical value as well as personal and emotional value. Words are not my tool to use in this venture, instead I will incorporate photographs, interviews, and records to describe these feelings.

The important part of this learning process remains in your hands. You must hear the records and performances of the people mentioned. Many are dead, others are alive and still performing.

Over the last years I've been fortunate to have lived with and learnt from Rev. Gary Davis, Mississippi John Hurt, Son House, Skip James, Fred McDowell, and Mance Lipscomb. All these men patiently explained their music in terms of their life and times. Other bluesmen who were just names on old 78's were revealed as real people. All of these musicians helped to formulate an American style of playing music on the acoustic guitar.

During the twenties and thirties these men were recorded by small record companies. When the depression hit the record business collapsed. Their music was presented as "race music." Music for the negro race. After forty years this music has become accepted and played by the white audience as well as being continued by many blacks. Who would have thought in 1930 that a record like *I'm So Glad* would ever find its way into the homes of millions of people. When Skip James first issued this record on the Paramount Record Company label only a few dozen were sold. Forty-five years after its first release Skip was able to watch the group "Cream" perform and record this tune.

I would like to thank Pete Whalen, Bernie Klatszko, Pete Kaufman, Richard Spottswood and Larry Cohn for making available their many rare old 78's. Together we have spent many hours discussing and listening to these old records.

For the many wonderful photographs used throughout this series I would like to thank Dick Waterman, Pete Whalen, Larry Cohn, Sam and Ann Charters, Chris Strachweiz, Herbert Grossman, Jack Prelutsky, Christine Brown and Georges Chatelain.

I have not attempted to delve into detailed discographical explanations of the individual songs presented. My main aim is to discuss guitar styles and techniques. I hope that these books will serve that purpose. For those interested in the history or discussions on the country blues I suggest you see Sam Charter's *The Bluesmen* or Stephan Calt's introduction to the *Country Blues Songbook*. Over the last years a wealth of material has been published concerning the lives of bluesmen and these can be found through the blues magazine *Blues Unlimited*.

The Country Blues Series will have five volumes. The first deals with Mississippi John Hurt and the Memphis sound, *Country Blues Guitar*. The second volume is a study into the music of the Mississippi Delta, *Delta Blues Guitar*. The third book deals with various ragtime blues guitarists, i.e. Blind Blake, Blind Lemon Jefferson, Blind Boy Fuller and Big Bill Broonzy, *Ragtime Blues Guitarists*. The fourth is a study into the blues and ragtime techniques of Rev. Gary Davis, *Rev. Gary Davis / Blues Guitar*. The fifth volume will discuss the blues styles of Texas, *Texas Blues Guitar*.

Hopefully all five volumes will stand as one. It is my hope that these books will help document the various regional acoustic blues guitar techniques and to show that an unique way of playing the guitar has been developed in America. A way of playing the guitar that is just as valid, exciting and detailed as the classical method or any other.

This study is not a spoon-feeding process. It will require much of your time and involvement. The end result will allow you to play in many country blues styles. It is my hope that from there you will go on to develop your own sound, style and techniques. You must listen to the various records and tapes available of the material presented.

This music has been a great part of my life. I hope some of the excitement I've found in it can be shared with you.

Peace,

Stefan Grossman

Preface

Reverend Gary Davis was a giant. He was a master guitar player. A wonderful and patient teacher who taught students his music and allowed them to perform in public when he felt the time was right. His students then did their part in enhancing his reputation, which was important to Rev. Davis.

An exciting performer who could entertain a college audience, bring to their feet 25,000 people at an outdoor festival, move the spirit of a few hundred men and women packed into a small Harlem store-front church, or bring smiles to a few students and friends who gathered around his home to hear his stories and music. He was an innovator in the story of the guitar. He was as important to the acoustic steel string guitar as Andres Segovia is to the Spanish guitar or Earl Scruggs to the Five-string banjo.

In the last decade the influence of his music has been felt on the broad pop level. Many of his arrangements and songs have been recorded by current popular artists. Taj Mahal, Hot Tuna, Donovan, Dave Van Ronk, Bob Dylan, Ralph McTell, and Peter, Paul and Mary are only a handful of groups and artists who have performed Rev. Davis' material. It is his guitar styles and techniques that have probably influenced today's music even more than his songs. He has been the teacher of many black and white guitarists. The sound usually associated with North Carolina guitar players, e.g. Blind Boy Fuller, can be traced back to the ideas and techniques that Rev. Davis perfected. Many young guitarists of today have either learned from him personally, his records or secondary sources and it is their playing that carries on his tradition.

As Rev. Davis used to say, "I have no children but I have sons."

I spent many years learning and documenting the styles and techniques of Rev. Davis. In 1960 I travelled to his home on 169th Street in the Bronx and introduced myself. Without any fanfare Rev. Davis took me under his wings and taught me the basics and intricacies of guitar playing. I spent two years studying his styles and methods. After that period I began to meet other black bluesmen, songsters and guitarists and started to branch out my studies to include the music of these musicians as well. However, Rev. Davis was always the center of my musical knowledge. I would go back to his home to play and discuss new songs I had learned. In fact, this action prompted Rev. Davis to show me many hidden tunes that he had either forgotten for a time or thought not interesting.

When I took Mississippi John Hurt up to Rev. Davis' home we spent hours talking and playing. The next day when John left for Washington, D.C. Rev. Davis showed me a host of tunes in a style similar to John's. A way of playing he called "some of that old time playing." Rev. Davis was a fancy guitar player and he hadn't realized that people of the new folk-revival audience also liked to hear simple picking. A similar experience occurred after I played him a tape of Bukka White playing some songs with a bottleneck. Rev. Davis looked down on this style but to show me that he could play it also, he asked his wife Annie for a glass cigar holder and began to play *Whistlin' Blues*. This is perhaps the most fascinating and interesting bottleneck-tuning, and piece, I have ever learned.

Rev. Davis was a competitor. He wanted to be the best guitarist. He always wanted to stay a few yards ahead of all his students. This he easily managed.

He played the five-string banjo, six-string banjo and harmonica. His first preference was the six-string guitar and "Miss Gibson" (his J-200 Gibson guitar). In his latter years he tended to favor playing the twelve-string guitar as it was somewhat easier.

Even in his last years Rev. Davis was an exciting guitarist and performer. He lost some of his speed in playing but this he replaced with a new emotional content. On hearing him perform at the Cambridge Folk Festival in 1971 I was amazed that all the intricacies of his playing were still present. He had wisely slowed down each tune so that he could play all the parts.

Rev. Davis died on May 5th, 1972. He was 76 years old. His death somehow came as a surprise to all the people who knew him well. He had seemed like a person who would live and play forever.

Fortunately, Rev. Davis recorded many records during his lifetime. He had a vast repertoire and much of this has been captured on discs.

My original intention when outlining the Country Blues Guitar Series was to have one volume devoted to the techniques of Rev. Davis. I had already put together a songbook of many of his tunes *Holy Blues / Rev. Gary Davis*, Robbins Music Publishers. When the time came to begin this project I realized that one volume would not comfortably hold all the material I thought essential in studying his many styles and techniques. I thought the best approach would be to write the books in the same way as Rev. Davis would teach a new student. In this way the first months were usually spent studying various blues, carnival show tunes and ragtime songs. It is this study that is included in this volume. The book is a study into the many blues and ragtime techniques that Rev. Davis perfected. Each key has a new approach and each approach usually has a few variations.

The continuation of this study will appear in a future volume. This will present more advanced styles as illustrated in many of the rags and show instrumentals from Rev. Davis' repetoire. The culmination of this study will be the arrangements Rev. Davis created for his many religious songs. These are fine examples of complex guitar playing at its best.

It is essential that you should hear a few of Rev. Davis' albums. The discography at the end of this book can be of help to you in this respect. A tape has also been prepared of the tunes presented in this volume and this is also highly recommended as it will make the learning process much more successful as well as supplying you with some great listening music.

I only hope that this book can give you the feel and spirit of Rev. Davis and his way of playing the guitar.

An Interview with Rev. Gary Davis

Life and Times

Q: When and where were you born?

A: *I was born on the last day of April, which is the thirtieth, in 1896. I was raised in Laurens County, South Carolina, on a farm, way down in the sticks, too. Way down in the country, so far you couldn't hear a train whistle blow unless it was on a cloudy day.*

Q: Who raised you?

A: *My grandmother mostly raised me. You see, my father gave me to my grandmother when I was a child because he knowed that there was no confidence to be put into my mother. She was always from one place to another, going from different towns and dances. Things like that. So my father gave me to my grandmother. I had one brother. He was a good guitar player. I taught him. He used to keep me up all night long to teach him how to play the guitar. He got killed in 1930. The woman he was going with killed him.*[1]

My mother had only two children that lived. She had eight children. All the others died when they were babes.

Q: Did your grandparents play instruments?

A: I didn't know anything about my grandfather on my mother's side. All I knew was them to play the harp. I had an Uncle who played guitar.

Q: Did he play well?

A: Long about them days what they called playing well wasn't what I could call playing well today.

Q: Did your Uncle ever show you how to play?

A: No, he never showed me nothing. Nobody ever showed me anything. I worked it out myself.

Q: Were you born blind?

A: Yes. My grandmother said I taken blind when I was three weeks old. The doctor had something put in my eyes that was too strong and that was what caused me to go blind.

Q: I thought you could see out of one eye?

A: I could tell the look of a person but to tell who it is, I'm not able to do that.

Q: What was the relationship between black and white folk down South when you were growing up?

A: You see, in those days white and colored didn't associate like the people here in the Northern states. I had too much experience about white folk then 'cause my grandmother always raised me up from white people. They always told me that it wasn't so good to dwell around white people's children. They loved to play with me but my grandmother didn't like me to take up too much time playing with white children.

I used to play for dances for white folks alright. When I was in the country I used to play for white folk's picnics. Everytime they'd have a picnic they'd come and get me.

Q: Tell me about the dances.

A: Sometimes people get drunk and get fightin' and shootin'. All like that happened. I would stop playing and find somewhere to go when that happened because you know me and bullets don't set horses.

Q: What type of tunes would you play?

A: I played everything I thought of. No religious songs though. Around then I was keen in my "young ways".

Q: Were you more interested in the lyrics or type of dance step that the people could do to your music?

A: Well it depended on what type of dance they had. You see ever since I started travelling cities, I found out things are different in the cities than it is in the country. In the country they had these old stomp down dances, you understand. Played on sets. They used to have fiddle players.

Q: Did you play different tunes at a white dance than at a black dance?

A: *You see, around then I played for most all of them. They were separate. I didn't make no exceptions unless it was something someone called for. There might be some slow song that the white people like to hear me play such like "love trots."*

Q: Did you go to school?

A: *Yeh, I was about 18 years old when I started going to school. School they call Cedar Springs for Blind People.*

Q: Did you go to school to learn how to read Braille?

A: *I went to Spartanburg, South Carolina. The Blind Institution. I was grown then, about 19 years old. My grandmother was still alive then.*

Q: How was it for a blind musician?

A: *Those that were experienced of music was alright. I never knew anyone but myself who practiced guitar, a blind person.*

Q: How did the people take to a blind person?

A: *I can only tell you what happened to me. The white people would always come around—and a nickel was something—and give me a nickel to play a song.*

Q: How did the black people treat you?

A: *Well, some of them promised like they do now!*

Q: When did you write *There Was A Time When I Went Blind*?

A: *Oh, that was a long time ago, in 1911. It's a gospel statement. It's speaking about what happened in my life. How people put me aside.*

Q: You thought that was because you were blind?

A: *When I was coming up, it was so.*

Q: What did you do as a kid, beside playing the guitar?

A: *I raised chickens and things like that. When the chickens seen me coming, you understand, they'd light up off the ground, light up on top of me. They didn't know what it was all about, but I did.*

Q: When did you leave Laurens County?

A: *After I married. Me and my first wife started travelling. I was playing from town to town. Anywhere! Playing on the streets then. I would get run off by the police more times than I can remember. But I played a long time before that laws been originated in the South. After I started travelling, thinking over my back life, my past life and the beginning of my life, I brought them all up together, all that mattered about my life. I had me some time to wonder. A man, good health, young, I couldn't admit who would want me for anything. That used to worry me. But as I started to travel I soon got out of that. You could tell when everybody would see me walking down the street with a woman that they wouldn't bite their*

9

tongues at all. They asked, "can't you do no better." You understand, they thought it was a disgrace for a woman to be walking with a blind man. They thought it a shame for a woman to take up time with a blind man.

Q: Tell me about your travelling around.

A: *I met a good many musicians.*

Q: Did you notice that in different areas there were different guitar styles?

A: *That's quite natural because I had a different style myself. I sat down and figured mine out. I always did sit down and study what way I could take advantage of a thing, trying to make it different than anybody else.*

Q: You didn't mind teaching people?

A: *No, I didn't mind teaching anything that they wanted to know that I knew.*

Q: There were a lot of musicians who copied your style?

A: *Yeh, I didn't keep up with their names.*

Q: What happened to your first wife?

A: *Well, that's a long story. The truth of it is that I found out she wasn't my wife but everybody' elses' wife. I let her go. We weren't getting along too well and after I found out her husband was living, that settled it for me. Yeh, I got married again. I've been married now longer than you've been here!*

Q: What made you leave the South and Durham, North Carolina?

A: *I didn't have no people there. All my people were gone so I travelled up to New York. The first place I lived was Mamaroneck, N.Y. That was in 1940. I came down to the city later on in the year and lived at 169th Street for 18 years.*

Q: Did you also play on the streets of New York?

A: *Yeh, it's a problem. Reason it's a problem you see, we weren't allowed to play out on the streets. Sometimes the police chased me and I'd take a chance and try to play again. Also I had guitars stolen off me as fast as I could get them.*

The Blues

Q: When was the first time you heard a blues?

A: *That broke out in 1910. I couldn't tell you where it came from. I first heard them from a fellow coming down the road picking a guitar and playing what you call "the blues." When I started playing the guitar there was no such thing as a piece coming out called "the blues." They played other songs. The blues, they just began to originate themselves.*

Q: Did you ever hear of W.C. Handy?

A: *No, I ain't never heard of him.*

Q: Who was one of the first bluesmen you heard?

A: *A fellow named Porter Irving. He played that song about Delia. He was born in South Carolina from where I come from.*

10

Old sow woke up one morning, found all her pigs dead.
Old sow said to the bull, run! we're bound to move our bed.
All the friends I had are gone.

Oh Delia, why don't you run,
Here comes that sheriff with a 44 Gatlin' gun.
All the friends I had are gone.

Take old Delia to the cemetery, bring me a rubber tired hack.
Put her in the ground, poor girl, she could never get back.
All the friends I had are gone.

Q: Why do you think people started to play the blues?

A: *Now, people had different feelings, you understand. He worried about a woman, or worried about a man, something like that. Get all stirred up in a cauldron. Thing like that is the blues.*

Q: They never felt that way before?

A: *No, they didn't have that before. They didn't have that name before. People have always been worried.*

Q: Did blues playing start on the guitar first?

A: *They started playing it on the piano too.*

Q: In church why can't you sing a blues?

A: *Folk music and blues is a whole lot of differences. That's like your singing some type of love-trot. If you do like the people wants you to do, you won't do nothing! You know that. Folk music is kind of like a love-trot. It's telling a story. Talk about the blues that leads you to the point of where a person is worried about somebody.*

Q: What would you tell a guitar student about playing blues?

A: *Well a lot of things I could tell a person if I just had the time to study what they were fishing for. To play blues on a guitar I'd teach them to play the guitar like a piano.*

Q: What do you think of bottleneck playing?

A: *I don't think nothing of that! You're cheating your own self. It ain't so respectable. People thinks it's a pretty thing but it's not.*

Q: Did you ever play with a bottleneck?

A: *Not too much for I didn't care for it.*[2]

Q: Did you ever try playing blues on the piano?

A: *No. Fact is I didn't know too much about piano until I got started travelling. I didn't even know how a piano was shaped. I didn't have no time for piano or organ. I stuck to the guitar, because I could carry that with me. I couldn't carry no piano!*

Blind Boy Fuller and Recording for ARC

Q: Tell me about Blind Boy Fuller.

A: His home was in Rockingham, North Carolina. He came up to Durham later. When I first run across him he didn't know how to play but one piece and that was with a knife. He wanted to take some of my training. I'd sit down and he'd come up to my house everyday and sit down and play. I taught him how to play. He would have been alright if I kept him under me long enough.

I knew his wife first. He had gotten away from her. She come to my house, I met her in the streets the first time, lookin' for him. I took her home with me to my mother's house. She had been out all night long and hadn't slept yet. Gave her my bed so she could lay down and sleep. Next day she happened to stumble up upon him, you know. He had got away from her and she didn't know where he was. She was awful fond of him. She was crazy about him. She never wanted to get too far from him. I can't talk too much about it because you women know how it is, even if you ain't married! When you come across somebody that you love you like to keep them close to you.

In the end he had to shoot her as she got too bad and out of hand.[3]

Q: Were you singing blues then?

A: Oh yeh, I was a "blues cat" then. What I mean by "blues cat" is that I played blues and blues and blues again and again. I would go to parties, dances and things like that. Chittlin' struts and all that kind of stuff.

Q: Was Fuller playing with anyone special in Durham, N.C.?

A: If I met him playing with anybody it was Sonny Terry. That's the only one I knew he played with.

Q: Tell me about recording for ARC.

A: We got together with this white man, Jimmy Long, who wanted somebody to come to New York City and make records. The first trip we all went together— Blind Boy Fuller, Bull City Red and myself. We stayed on the corner of 133rd Street and 7th Avenue.

Q: Did you like the recording session?

A: I didn't enjoy it too well and I enjoyed it alright too. I couldn't hardly catch on to it until later on. They'd give you beer to drink but I didn't want any liquor. I played a steel bodied guitar then. There was a difference between me and the "man." He paid the rest of them but didn't want to give me all of mine. That was the difference between us.

The records were just like you put it out. You had to go over each song as much as twice.

Q: How much did they pay you?

A: They didn't give us nothing of what we should have got! Forty dollars for us and $35 for Bull City Red.

Q: Who was Bull City Red?

A: His name was George Washington but we called him Bull City Red. He played the guitar and sometimes he tried to play washboard. He sings I Saw The Light From Heaven Come Down *on my record.*

Q: Where was Jimmy Long from?

A: He was from Burlington, North Carolina.

Q: What type of songs did you record?

A: *I couldn't tell you about them all. I made ten Christian songs and two sets of blues—*Moutain Jack Blues *and* Ice Pick Blues. *Fuller put out the song about "The Stuff Is Here" and another one about "The little red rooster said to the little red hen to meet him down at the barn at half-past ten." He put out another song about "Sure as you're born Ida, somebody's been playing with that thing."*[4]

Q: How did Fuller die?

A: *He suffered a kidney trouble. That's what killed him. His thigh wasn't as big as this guitar neck here. That's the way he went away.*

About Songs and Musicians

Q: Tell me about some of the guitar players you liked back in the early days.

A: *I knew Willie Walker, you see. We all lived in the same city together, Greenville, South Carolina. He was a master guitar player. I didn't ever learn his pieces. He was a good singer also. Most I heard him play was the blues like* Crow Jane. *Him and Simmie Dooley both were good guitar players. Simmie Dooley he lived in Spartanburg, South Carolina.*

Simmie Dooley also played with Pink Anderson. I met Simmie several times. He could play the guitar good too, though not like Willie Walker.

I ain't never heard anybody on a record yet beat Blind Blake on the guitar. I like Blake because he plays right sporty. Blind Lemon Jefferson plays like he wants somebody to feel sorry for him.

Q: What did you think of Blake's guitar style?

A: *It's a nice style. He plays in that piano style. I and him both plays on the same orders. His favorite keys were G and C and A (I can't recall what songs he played in A but he did). I'd sit down and listen to some of his performances—records.*

Q: What happened to Blake?

A: *Blind Blake got killed. I don't know exactly when, but I think a year before I came to New York City in 1930. People told me a street car run him over. I don't know how true it was!*

Q: Were there other guitar players who played in his style?

A: *Yeh, Buddy Moss and Bill Broonzy.*

Q: Did you ever meet Big Bill?

A: *Yeh, one time before he died. I was up there in Harlem, 125th Street where Brownie McGee had a music studio. I didn't have no opinion about Big Bill, 'cause I found him fine. He was a good guitar player. He played on the orders of Blake on some things but he didn't have a bass like Blake. But he was tolerable good—awful good!*

Q: And Buddy Moss?

A: *Well, when Fuller was starting to make records most of anything he come to know about was Buddy Moss' songs. They would re-arrange them and have him play them over. That's how Fuller got started.*

Q: Did you record *Ice Pick Blues* in the old days?

A: *No—Oh yes I did. In the old days when I played for the Perfect Record Company (ARC).*

Q: How about Jim Jackson?

A: *I ain't never heard Jim Jackson play anything but* Kansas City Blues *and he messed that up!*

Q: Tell me about *Candyman.*

A: *That song came out in 1905 in a carnival show. I couldn't tell you too much about the old carnival shows as I never worked at one. I did get some music from some of them. They used to have names like "Robertson Show" and all different kinds of shows.*

Q: Could you play *Rag Mama, Rag?*

A: *Do you know why I hardly never do anything like that? Because its cheap guitar playing stuff. I don't play no cheap stuff.*

Q: Tell me about *Goin' To Germany.*

A: *I heard a white girl downtown singing that song. Downtown in Greenwich Village a couple of years ago, before I moved off of Park Avenue. A little girl sung that and they didn't have nobody who knew how to get that thing together with. They didn't know how to get that thing stuck together, so I said, "Let me have your guitar, I'll show you how." You know some people who don't have a thing don't know how to do it.*

Q: What about *Save Up Your Money?*

A: *Let me see about that. That came out in 1905. Did you ever hear: "You buck up to me, and I buck up to you way down in Georgia. The big camp meeting took place at the color of the race, way down in Georgia." I was a small kid, no more than three years old when that song came out.*

Q: Tell me about *West Coast Blues* by Blind Blake. What's the trick in playing a tune like that?

A: *It's the bass you touch that makes it roll. It ain't that hard. Blake could play that thing. He could play.*

Q: What about *Soldier's Drill.* When did you write that?

A: *Let's see, way before I got married the first time. Before I knew anything about marrying a woman. Way back. 1918.*

Q: A song like *Saddle It Around,* where did that come from?

A: *That come when I was a child. I heard a lady and her husband play that song. Her name was Clara Fowles and her husband's name was Crete. I also heard* Little Boy Who Made Your Britches *when I was a child.*

On Guitar Playing

Q: Could you tell me about your way of playing the guitar?

A: *Well you see, you've got three hands to play a guitar and only two for a piano. Well, your forefinger and your thumb—that's the striking hand, and your left hand is your leading hand. Your left hand tells your right hand what strings to touch, what changes to make. That's the greatest help! You see, one hand can't do without the other.*

14

Q: I always thought that your guitar styles tried to imitate the piano.

A: *Well, that's the way I always play the guitar. It's suppose to be played just like your playing a piano.*

Q: How come you use only two fingers to pick the guitar?

A: *Because that's all you need.*

Q: Do you think guitar students should use only two fingers also?

A: *That's what I use. I teach them the same as me.*

Q: Does using two fingers give you a certain sound?

A: *It is a certain sound. You're going to talk about it, you see. You don't give the rest of your hand time to do nothing if you play with all of your fingers.*

Q: Were you using finger-picks when you started playing the guitar?

A: *Oh no, I started using them about 25 years ago—or longer.*

Q: Were you using finger-picks when you recorded for Perfect Record Company in 1935?

A: *Yes.*

Q: Do you think its better to use finger-picks?

A: *It saves your fingers!*

Q: When do you think a guitarist should practice?

A: *Well, to love for anything to come to you—you practice early in the morning, at 7 o'clock until 8, and than put down your guitar. At 8 o'clock in the evening until 9 you practice again. After that you should concentrate.*

Q: Why so early in the morning?

A: *That's because when music comes to you early in the morning your members are alright. There's nothing to stir you, to disturb you. By 8 o'clock everything is going on.*
    At 8 o'clock at night everything is once again pretty still. By 9 you can call it bedtime—something like that.

Q: What type of guitar do you like?

A: *Any types that's good to play. Don't make any difference what type of guitar as long as it is a good one. I like a guitar that I can just slip down on to—with a good action. A hard playing guitar will make your fingers sore. You know something about that, don't you.*

Q: Where did you learn how to play?

A: *Well, I was in the South when I learned the guitar. I practically picked it up myself. I made my first guitar out of a tin can. I was a boy about ten years old.[5] I drove me a hole in each end of the pie-pan, run me up a stick through there, that's the way I made it.*

Q: Did anybody show you how to play?

A: No, I learned all by myself. My motto's always been—to bring out something somebody else hadn't heard before. I always loved to do things different than anybody else did.

Q: Did you ever put down the guitar?

A: Well, for three years I didn't have no guitar, that's when I was a boy. There was a time also when I broke my right hand wrist. That was in North Carolina. I was carrying on a revival and I slipped down. I was going along one night and there was snow on the ground. When I stepped up on a bank of snow and my foot slipped and to keep from falling I was shuffling around. I struck my hand on an iron-water dog. I didn't know it was broken until I went to the doctor the next morning. He told me it was broke. He put me up on a table and put me asleep. When I woke up he had a cast slammed up to my elbow.

I lost the use of that hand a long time. I thought I was never going to be able to play no more—but I did![6]

Q: Did you ever play twelve string guitar?

A: First twelve string guitar I run across was in 1920. Never heard tell of one before. I went to the store and asked the man to show it to me and I found out how it was tuned. I played it just like I played a six string guitar.

Q: Were a lot of guitarists playing twelve string back in those days?

A: Yeh! but them guitars didn't have much of a good action. They were mostly old Stellas.

Q: When is the right time for a guitar player to perform in public?

A: God never called anybody to preach when he didn't have any words to say. It's no use offering yourself to somebody. If they want you, they'll call you.

You can go find a lot of puppies, you understand. They all belong to the same dog. When you lay eyes on those puppies you can tell which one is going to be on top. You can pick that one out. You can see something in that one you don't see in the rest.

Don't you go picking yourself out to the people. It's them that pick you out.

Q: Do you find it hard to perform?

A: Ain't no easy job to sit down and play guitar no how! Some of the people that look at it think it's easy, because it looks easy to them.

Q: How do you approach playing the guitar?

A: I sit down and study how to take advantage of a guitar, you see.

Q: What advice would you give to guitar students?

A: You know you can't give a two week old baby peas and corn-bread. You've got to give it what its able to eat. Lot of people come here wanting me to teach them things but they're not able to stand up to it.

I'm subject to mistakes. All of us are. Sometimes you're going East and you're actually going West. That's the way it happens with all of us sometimes. Mistakes is the best stop in life. You know too much you understand, then you done made a mistake already.

You be too perfect then the mistakes been already made. But you go try to do a thing and make a mistake to start off with, then that's the best start in life. It gives somebody a chance to correct you.

Afterthought

Q: How do you feel about the times now?

A: *Just like I think about the times passed. There was a time in this time. This here is the time in this time.*

Q: Is life better for you now?

A: *I don't know whether life is any better. I had the same life as the times that passed.*

Notes

1. In another interview Rev. Davis stated that his mother "would go to town and cook for the white folks and my father stayed in trouble all the time. That's why he gave me to my grandmother because he was in trouble all the time."   And in yet another interview Rev. Davis said that his father died before "he could realize him too much."

2. One of the most exciting and interesting bottleneck tunes I have ever heard was Rev. Davis' *Whistlin' Blues*. Even though Rev. Davis looked down on this style he had nevertheless perfected it and extended it to give a unique sound all his own. This was rather typical of Rev. Davis' approach to music.

3. Fuller sung about this in his *Big House Bound* (Vocalion 04897) and *Crooked Woman Blues* (Vocalion 05527).

4. From the ARC records it shows that Rev. Davis recorded the following tunes of which only one was never issued:
    Cross And Evil Woman Blues / I'm Throwin' Up My Hand, ARC 35-10-16
    I Am The True Vine / I Am The Light Of The World, ARC 5-12-66
    Oh Lord Search My Heart / You Got To Go Down, ARC 35-10-33
    I Saw The Light / Lord, Stand By Me, ARC 6-05-65
    Twelve Gates To The City / You Can Go Home, ARC 7-04-55
    Have More Faith In Jesus / The Angel's Message To Me, ARC 6-11-63
    I Belong To The Band, Hallelujah / The Great Change In Me, ARC 6-02-65
    Lord, I Wish I Could See, unreleased

    Rev. Davis constantly referred to *I'm Throwin' Up My Hands* as *Mountain Jack Blues* and *Cross And Evil Woman Blues* as *Ice Pick Blues*. In fact in both tunes there are verses that use the corresponding titles that Rev. Davis gave the tunes, i.e. in *I'm Throwin' Up My Hands* the first line of the song is "If I could holler just like a mountain jack," and the last line of *Cross And Evil Woman Blues* is "All she wants is a shotgun or razor, ice-pick or pistol she can find."

5. In an earlier interview Rev. Davis stated that he began to play the guitar at the age of seven.

6. This was an interesting fact to discover. Rev. Davis' left hand wrist seemed to have set out of position (it was a little to the left of its axis). This enabled him to play many unusual chord positions.

The Tablature System

"...Learning from listening is unquestionably the best way, the only way that suits this kind of music. You're setting the notes down for a record of what happened, a record that can be studied, preserved and so on—a necessary and useful companion to the recordings of the actual sounds. I keep thinking of this as I transcribe; if you could do it, it would be good to have a legend across each page reading:

Listen to the record if you want to learn the song."

Hally Wood
taken from the Publisher's Foreword to the *New Lost City Ramblers Song Book*

I began to play music at an early age. The formality and coldness of the teaching methods as well as the dull material brought a quick end to my interest. The printed music page seemed a strange and difficult language to master. Anyway, who was interested in *Autumn Leaves* or *Tea For Two?* The songs had no personal appeal for me. Five years later I once again picked up a guitar and started to play. This time I wisely shied away from organized music theory. Sounds from my head found their way to the guitar. I concentrated on playing and not on learning about sharps, flats, time signatures, key changes and chord structures. I didn't want to be cramped by words.

A few months after that, I found myself sitting in front of Rev. Gary Davis, learning how to play from him.

For two years I concentrated on the many styles Rev. Davis patiently taught me. I spent hours up at his house breathing in thick cigar smoke, eating Mrs. Davis' cooking and learning incredible songs. It was during this time that I devised a method for writing down the songs Rev. Davis was teaching me. I needed this so that I could learn more in a lesson and remember it all. So instead of two songs a day I was able to absorb five. The system I developed showed only the fret positions of the strings. The sound, rhythm, and accent of the piece were all in my head. My system depended on hearing the song. The chord positions were drawn or rather scribbled out so that no fingering problems would arise.

The tablature presented here is a culmination of the system developed at Rev. Davis' house. Instead of sketches I have photographs of hand positions. The system still relies on hearing the piece of music. All of the items presented here are available either on record or on tape. The sources are all listed before each song and in the discography at the end of each volume.

I am reminded of the words of the great Sufi Hazrat Inayat Khan:

"...The traditional ancient songs of India composed by great Masters have been handed down from father to son. The way music is taught is different from the Western Way. It is not always written, but it is taught by imitation. The teacher sings and the pupil imitates, and all the intricacies and subtleties are learned by imitation."

It is this theme that I have tried to transpose into the tablature system.

Now for the tablature:

Each space indicates a string:

1 means the high E
2 means the B (or second string)
3 means the G string
4 means the D string
5 means the A string
6 means the low E string

A number on this space indicates the fretted position. A *zero* would mean open string. The number *1* indicates the first fret of that string. (Note the diagram below.) The *zero* on the second string indicates that the open second string should be played. The *1* placed on the third string's space indicates first fret on the third string. Likewise *4* placed on the fourth string's space indicates fourth fret of the fourth string.

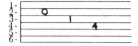

All the volumes of this series are concerned with fingerpicking guitar styles. These are generally played with the thumb, index and middle fingers of the right hand (presuming that you are right-handed). To indicate which finger to use, flags are placed next to the numbers that show fretted positions. A flag down means that the thumb strikes the note. If the flag is up then your index or middle finger (whichever you prefer) should strike the note. The choice will clarify itself when playing a song up to tempo.

The diagram below shows an open sixth string played with the thumb and the second fret of the third string played with the index finger.

In most cases the thumb will play an alternating bass usually on the top three bass strings. The index and middle finger will play notes on the first, second and third strings. But again these aren't rules and there are many exceptions.

In fingerpicking there are two choices. Either we pinch two notes together or we don't (also called a pluck in some books). A pinch is shown by connecting the two notes with a line. A variation of this comes when two treble notes are pinched with a bass note.

In the above example we have from left to right the following: first the open sixth string is played by the thumb. Next the first fret of the sixth string is pinched together with the third fret of the third string. The sixth string is plucked by the thumb and the third by the index finger. Next the thumb strikes the third fret of the fourth string. This is similar to an alternating bass pattern. The next notes are the first fret sixth string played by the thumb. This is pinched with two notes in the treble. The index and middle finger strike the first fret first string and the third fret second string. The next note is the index finger hitting the first fret second string. Lastly we have the bass note played with the thumb on the third fret fourth string.

In blues many times the notes are not decisively played. The tablature makes this clear.

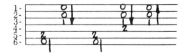

In the first case the thumb hits the open sixth string but the second fret on the fifth string also sounds. This is done simply by playing harder on the sixth string. The force will make the fifth string vibrate. This technique is done in the bass as well as treble section of a song. Next we see an arrow. This indicates a brush. The direction is found in the arrowhead. If pointed up, the hand brushes up towards the sixth string. If down, the hand brushes down to the first string. The amount of strings to be affected are shown by the length of the arrow. For instance the next group of notes shows a brush up towards the sixth string of the open first, open second and first fret third string. Next is the bass open sixth string with the vibrating fifth. Next is an arrow up. Again we brush up towards the sixth string but this time the second fret of the fourth string vibrates and sounds. It is not hit but is affected by the other three notes. This effect is gotten by dampening the strings with your right hand palm or by an upward stroke of the right hand. This sound is difficult to explain. But in many pieces you can hear notes sounding yet you know distinctly that they are not being hit. This is in the nature of the guitar. By hitting one note it will set other notes to sound. The last notes in this example are a brush down to the first string of the open first, open second, and first fret third string.

Now let's look at the same example with the chord letter and chord picture added. The first indicates what chord it is. The circled number indicates which photograph this fingering corresponds to.

2— E Chord

In order to keep the tablature from being cluttered up with circles I did not include them in a repeated segment of a piece. I presume you will remember the positions. The chords are given where I think helpful. Some finger positions have involved chord designations. Instead of complicating the song with this additional information I let the photographs tell you what is needed. Once you have learned the music you can go back and learn the theory.

There are certain effects used in blues guitar that are also symbolized in the tablature. Here are some examples; explanations follow.

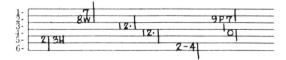

a. The hammer-on. Here the fret hammered is placed after the flag. In this case the second fret is played by the thumb and then the third fret is hammered. This is all done in one continuous motion and produces a single sound.

b. The wham or slurred note. This is designated by a "w". In this case the eighth fret second string is whammed and played with the seventh fret first string. Both notes are played with index and middle fingers respectively.

c. The harmonic. This is symbolized by a dot (•). The two notes are both harmonics. The first is the twelfth fret third string played by index finger. The next is the twelfth fret fourth string hit by the thumb.

d. The slide. This is shown by a dash (—). This reads: second fret sixth string slides to fourth fret sixth string. These notes are struck by the thumb.

e. The pull off. This shows the note pulled off and what remains. The letter "P" designates this effect. The last note reads: ninth fret second string is pulled off against the seventh fret second string. Also we are pinching the open fourth string with our thumb.

This sounds wordy and complicated. But once you become familiar with the tablature it will all become very simple and automatic. All of my students end up sight-reading the tablature. The photos will illuminate the positions in these effects. As for tonality and accent, these are for you to hear in the originals.

The vertical lines in the tablature are meant to separate musical phrases. It is at these points that I would like you to stop and to repeat the sections already studied. In this way you can slowly build up a tune by putting together all of these passages. These vertical lines should not be confused with musical bar lines. The tab shows no indication of bar structure or rhythmic notation.

Tablature is intended for those people who want to learn how to play first and learn theory second. Tablature can help you to find the notes, while the records can give you the feel of a song. Then it's up to you to put the song together. Your fingers and your touch are your own. These are unique and will produce your own sound no matter how hard you try to imitate.

Many students ask me how to hold the right hand while finger-picking. The Classical and Flamenco styles have rigid rules in this context. Our only guide is comfort. What is comfortable is usually the best position. I would like to point out one similarity that many great guitarists have in this respect. From such artists as Reverend Gary Davis, John Hurt, Son House and Skip James to Dave Laibman, Martin Carthy, Bert Jansch and Steve Mann, all rest their third and fourth fingers on the guitar face. This technique will reinforce your sound and give you a freedom to accent heavily when necessary. I suggest you experiment with it.

Good luck and I hope you enjoy all the music in this volume.

Peace,

Stefan Grossman

Blues Guitar of Rev. Gary Davis

Saddle It Around

Key: G
Section transcribed: The guitar part played with each verse.
Source: Black Patty Tape Service

This is a simple guitar piece played with an alternating bass technique. The tune is picked around a G chord. This arrangement is similar to John Hurt's *Spike Driver's Moan* in many ways. The only difficult passage might be at the end of the second line of tablature. Here the second fret of the third string is first hammered-on and than pulled-off. This section might take some practice in order to smoothly fit into the tune.

The guitar instrumental plays an additional line. This is a repeat of the second and third lines of tablature.

Arranged and Adapted by Rev. Gary Davis

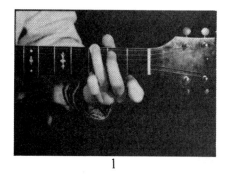

1

2

Saddle It Around

Won't you tell me where you come _ from _ now. _

Sad - dle it a - round, just sad - dle it a - round. Tell ___

___ me where we come from ___ now. ___

Sad - dle it a - round, just sad - dle it a - round.

Tell me where you on your way to
Saddle it around, just saddle it around
Tell me where you on your way to
Saddle it around, just saddle it around

Give my horse some water
Saddle it around, just saddle it around
Please give him some fodder
Saddle it around, just saddle it around

I got in a little town, got arrested
Saddle it around, just saddle it around
Put me in the jailhouse
Saddle it around, just saddle it around

That morning they tried me
Saddle it around, just saddle it around
They give me six months for vagrancy
Saddle it around, just saddle it around

Turn me loose Judge I ain't never been here before
Saddle it around, just saddle it around
I'll give you twelve months, don't come back here
    no more
Saddle it around, just saddle it around

That old Judge was cruel to me
Saddle it around, just saddle it around
He wouldn't let me loose and go
Saddle it around, just saddle it around

Cocaine Blues / Coco Blues

Key: C
Section transcribed: Cocaine Blues has the second verse guitar part written
    out.
    Coco Blues has the first verse and bridge transcribed.
*Source: Cocaine Blues–Lo' I Be With You Always–*Kicking Mule Records
    *Coco Blues–Pure Religion and Bad Company–*77 Records

Rev. Davis' arrangement for *Cocaine Blues* is perhaps one of his most widely imitated pieces. I have used two sources to show the various possibilities of the tune. The first is taken from a version where Rev. Davis played and sang the song. *Coco Blues* is taken from an instrumental version. For some reason the record company titled the tune incorrectly as *Coco Blues.*

This is the type of playing that Rev. Davis' referred to as "old time playing." It is played using an alternating bass technique and in the key of C. The first difference to note in playing this arrangement is that the bass alternates from a fourth to sixth string pattern. Usually when playing a C chord we alternate from a fifth, fourth, sixth, and fourth pattern. (This approach is discussed in some detail in the Country Blues Guitar book.) The bass pattern that Rev. Davis establishes is unique in that the bass becomes reversed as we start from the fourth string. This gives the tune a special flavour.

The transcription of *Cocaine Blues* should be easy to follow. The only difficult passage might be the F section. It is important to accent the even beats heavily as this will give the song its correct feel.

For *Coco Blues* I have transcribed two sections. The first is similar to *Cocaine Blues.* This is the guitar part played behind the verses. I have included this so that you can study another variation of playing this part. The second transcribed section is the bridge. This part has always fascinated me. The lead in chord of C^7 adds a new coloring to the arrangement and makes the piece quite beautiful. In fact, this simple guitar arrangement stands very well as an instrumental.

I have written out three sets of lyrics for this song. This is one of the few pieces of Rev. Davis that tended to be sung differently every time he performed it.

Cocaine Blues was a very popular tune in the twenties and versions by the Memphis Jug Band, Luke Jordan and others have been recorded. It is sometimes titled *Take A Whiff On Me.*

Cocaine Blues

Words and music by Rev. Gary Davis

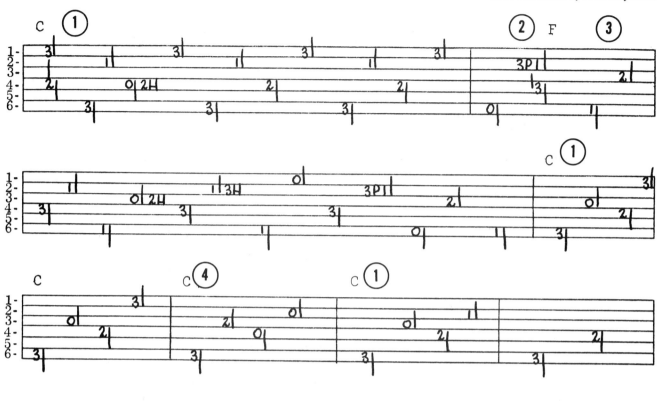

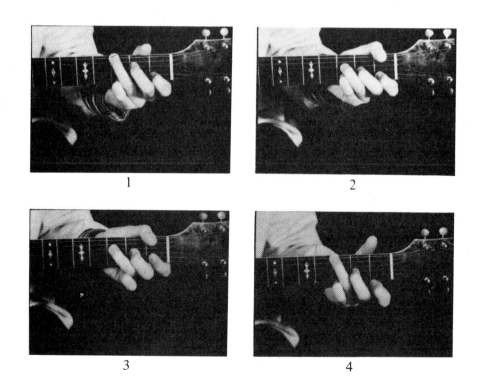

1

2

3

4

Coco Blues

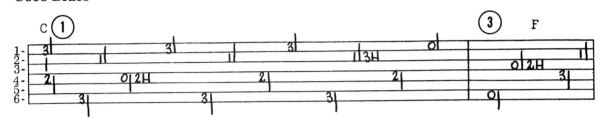

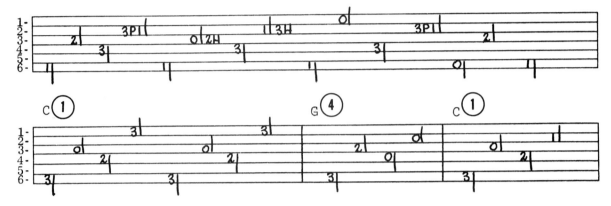

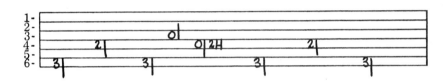

Bridge (Guitar Break):

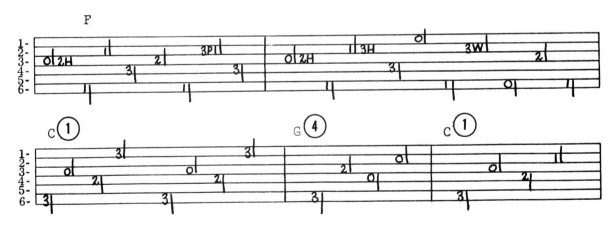

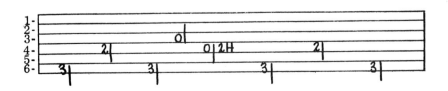

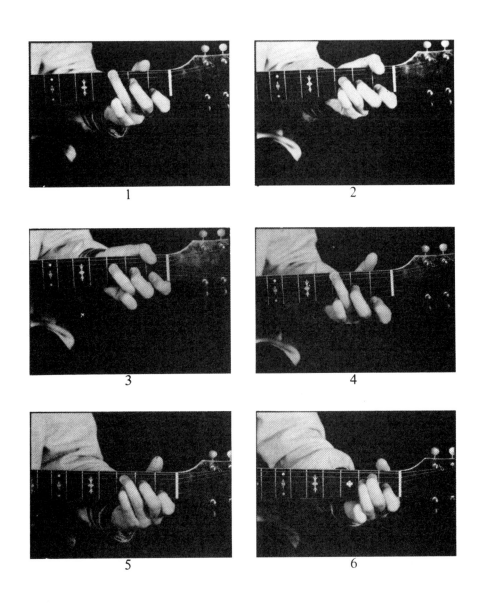

Cocaine Blues

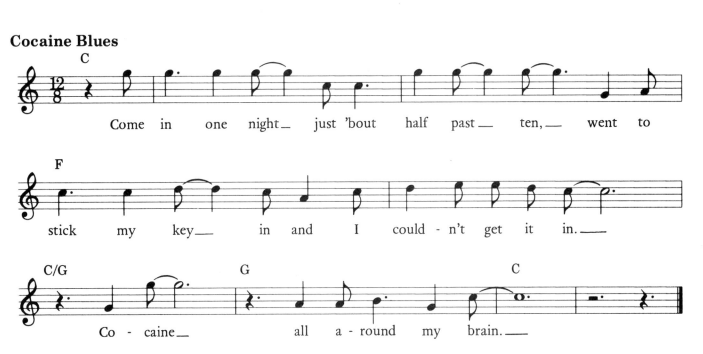

Come in one night — just 'bout half past — ten, — went to stick my key — in and I could-n't get it in. — Co - caine — all a - round my brain. —

Cocaine Blues

From *Let Us Get Together*
on Kicking Mule Records

spoken introduction:
Alot of people don't know what's a matter with
them sometime if nobody can't get along with
them, you know. I'm here to tell you, cocaine
done got all around my brain.

Come in one night just about half past ten
Went to stick my key in and I couldn't get in
Cocaine all around my brain

Come in one evening just about half past nine
My gal got a chair and tried to knock me blind
Cocaine done got all around my brain

What's that coming yonder looking so red
My gal coming with a gun, wanting to kill me
    dead
Cocaine done got all around my brain

I said, run here somebody, won't you please run
    in a hurry
This cocaine done got me worried
Cocaine done got all around my brain

Been out all night long and ain't slept none yet
This cocaine has given me a fit
Cocaine done got all around my brain

I come in one morning just about half past four
My gal got a chair and knocked me right on out
    the door
Cocaine done got all around my brain

Said run here somebody, run here quick
This cocaine has got me sick
Cocaine done got all around my brain

From *Blues And Gospel*
on Biograph 12034

Woke up one morning just about half past four
Heard somebody knocking on my door
Cocaine done got all around my brain

I come in one morning just about half past ten
My gal got a chair tried to do her best
    to knock me in
Cocaine done got all around my brain

Found myself sitting on the side of the road
Just spent all the money I had
    for my room and board
Cocaine done got all around my brain

Run here mama, won't you run here quick
This cocaine's about to make me sick
Cocaine done got all around my brain

Woke up this morning about half past six
My gal done quit me, she done had got me fixed
Cocaine done got all around my brain

Been out all night long and I ain't slept none yet
This cocaine has done given me a fit
Cocaine done got all around my brain

Look'a here woman, the way you done me,
    it ain't going to do
If you don't do no better
    I'm going to have to kill it over you
Cocaine done got all around my brain

From a performance at the
Golden Vanity Folk Club, Boston, Mass. 1959

spoken introduction:
Some people drinks rum. Some people drinks
this here, home-made wine. Some people drinks
gin. All that kind of stuff, you understand.
Some folks taste a meal and some folk sniff
cocaine.

Way back yonder when I was a child I'd been
told of cocaine. Ever since I known what
drinking was. Used to be when they told me
of sniffing cocaine they'd put it on the point
of a knife and sniff it off the head, you
understand. They got the biggest kind of drunk.

Nowadays they have a way, sometimes they get it
in your vein and they call it like today narcotics.
Its the same name they give it
way back yonder—cocaine, but its the same
narcotic.

Sometimes I get to feel nothing but cocaine
but ain't had nothing to sniff. Sometimes
you get tired of being loved, you understand.
You got cocaine a'plenty. You don't have to sniff
none. Ain't that right!

I heard the boy say "I'm going uptown
   ain't going to hurry back"
He said "My baby got something I sure do lack"
Cocaine getting all around my brain

He said, "See that woman yonder,
   coming dressed in black"
I believe to my soul she's going to take me back"
Cocaine all around my brain

You ought to have been here a long time ago
Snuffing cocaine up the head
Cocaine all around my brain

Talking about your good gal, you ought to see
   mine
She ain't so pretty but she do just fine
Cocaine done got all around my brain

One of these mornings, it won't be long
You're going to wake up and call for me
   and I'll be gone
Cocaine done got all around my brain

All of these people ought to be like me
Drink that good corn whiskey and let the
   cocaine be
Cocaine done got all around my brain

"…I'm subject to mistakes. All of us are. Sometimes you're going East and your actually going West. That's the way it happens with all of us sometimes. Mistakes is the best stop in life. You know too much you understand, then you done made a mistake already.

31

Coco Blues

You Got The Pocket Book, I Got The Key

Key: C
Section transcribed: Verse and instrumental break.
Source: Black Patty Tape Service

After I had mastered *Cocaine Blues* I asked Rev. Davis if he knew any other pieces played in the key of C and in that "old time playing" style. He then proceeded to play *You Got The Pocket Book, I Got The Key*. This uses the same techniques and positions as *Cocaine Blues* but here a stronger melodic line is played against the reverse alternating bass.

Rev. Davis was unable to recall any of the lyrics to this song which seems unfortunate as the title is a beautifully phrased sentiment.

I have recorded this arrangement on a disc titled *How To Play Blues Guitar* (Transatlantic Records in Europe and Kicking Mule Records in the States). I was never able to get a tape of Rev. Davis performing this tune but hopefully one will pop up in the next years.

Both *Coacine Blues* and this arrangement take full advantage of hammer-on and pull-off techniques. To master these sounds I strongly suggest you hear the original recordings.

You Got The Pocket Book, I Got The Key

Music by Rev. Gary Davis

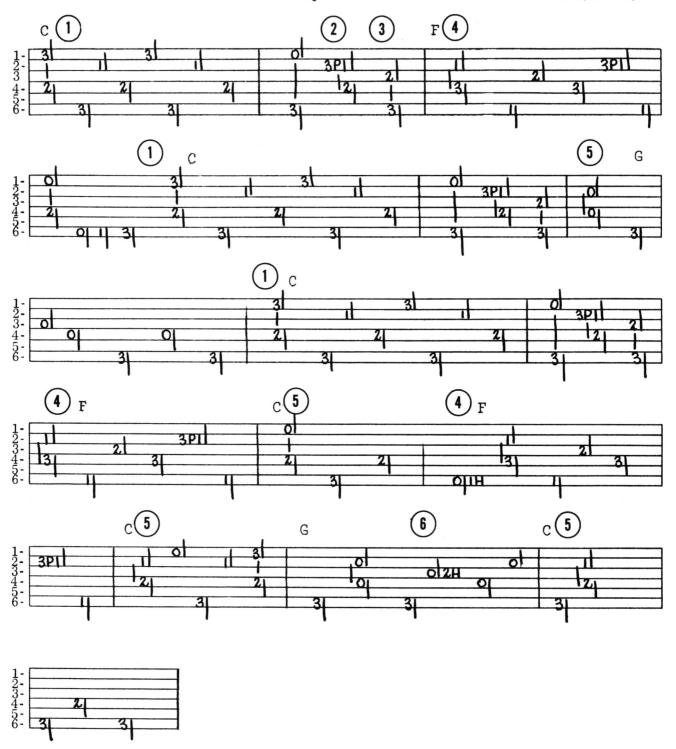

Bridge:

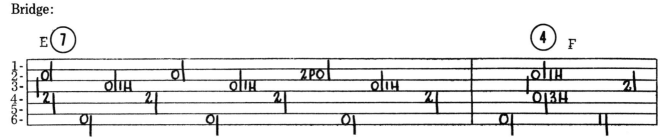

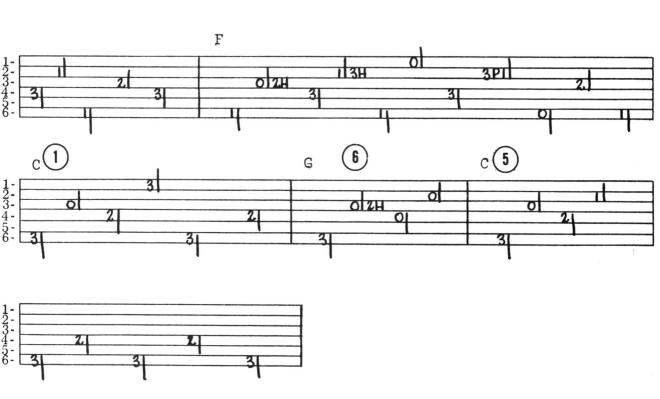

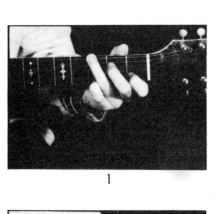

1

2

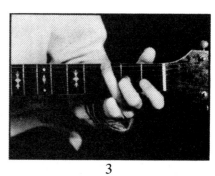

3

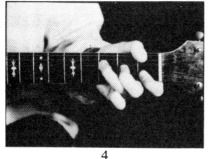

4

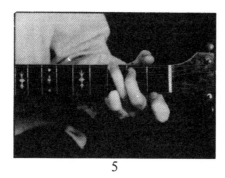

5

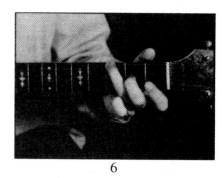

6

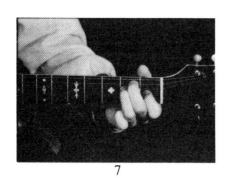

7

You Got The Pocket Book, I Got The Key

Lost Boy In The Wilderness

Key: G
Section transcribed: The instrumental introduction.
Source: Say No To The Devil—Prestige Bluesville

This song is a continuation of our study of playing in the key of G. *Saddle It Around* introduced this key and *Lost Boy In The Wilderness* takes the lesson a few steps further. In this arrangement we are still using an alternating bass pattern around a normal G chord. However, here our bass goes from the sixth to fourth strings and on the fourth bass note we fret the second fret of the fourth string.

This gives the alternating bass a new dimension. It creates a counter-point bass line in its simplest form. Against this pattern the melody of the tune is played on the treble strings. Over this complete arrangement the story of *Lost John* is told. (Usually Rev. Davis performed this tune with a harmonica.)

This arrangement is a culmination of the previous three songs and the techniques you should have developed in playing those. The end section of the tune has several hammer-on/pull-off notes that we have also played in *Saddle It Around.*

I have used the same approach as this arrangement, in arranging *East Colorado Blues* which can be heard on *Finger-Picking Guitar Techniques* (Transatlantic Records in Europe, Kicking Mule Records in the States.)

Music by Rev. Gary Davis

Lost Boy In The Wilderness

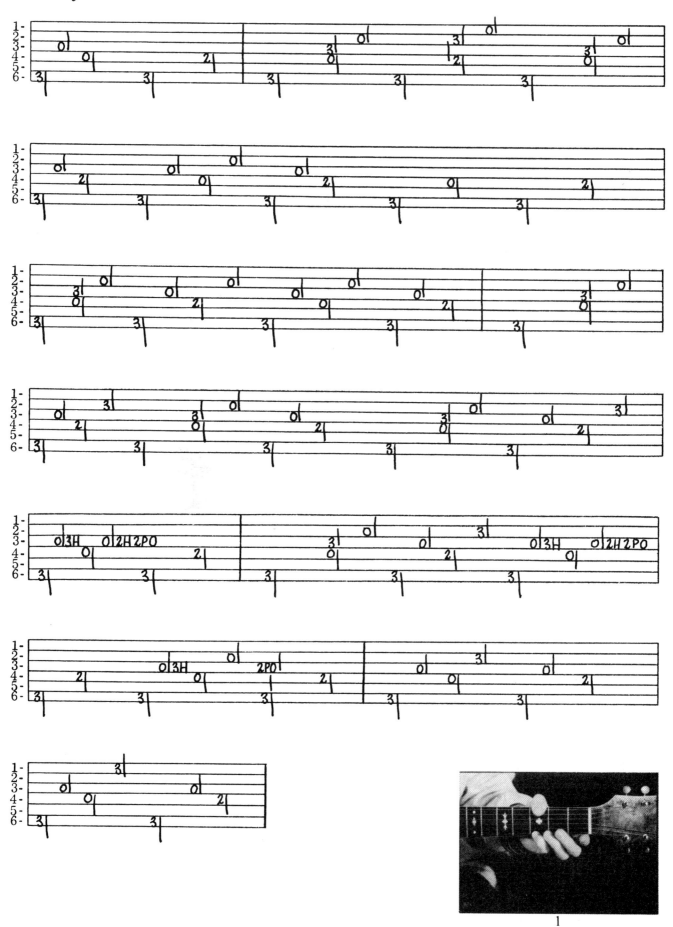

Lost Boy In The Wilderness

Candyman

Key: C
Section transcribed: Arrangement played behind the verses. An embellishment.
A variation of the end tag.
Source: Lo' I Be With You Always—Kicking Mule Records

This has become the most popular of Rev. Davis' songs. Donovan, Dave Van
Ronk, Bob Dylan and Hot Tuna have all recorded versions based on the playing
of Rev. Davis.

The arrangement extends the bass pattern introduced in *Lost Boy in the
Wilderness* for the key of C. This means that we have an alternating bass pattern with a simple counter-point line. The tune is played in the key of C and
should be thought of as having two parts. The first section uses a basic lick and
the second section begins when the F chord is introduced; here an alternating
bass pattern is played while a melodic line is picked out on the treble strings.

The basic lick in C has the bass alternating from the fifth to third strings.
First, the third string is played open and then fretted on the second fret. This is
clearly indicated in the tab.

This lick changes somewhat when the G^7 chord is played in that the bass
now goes from the sixth to third strings.

The last two lines of the song are played straight forward. I have also written out a variation of this section.

Also transcribed is an embellishment that Rev. Davis would play while
playing the C chord in the first part. This is quite a challenge to master.

Fortunately, there appears on the album *Lo' I Be With You Always* a very
complete performance of *Candyman*. Here we can hear the song being sung as well
as several guitar variations of the basic theme. I suggest you hear this version.

Candyman

Words and music by Rev. Gary Davis

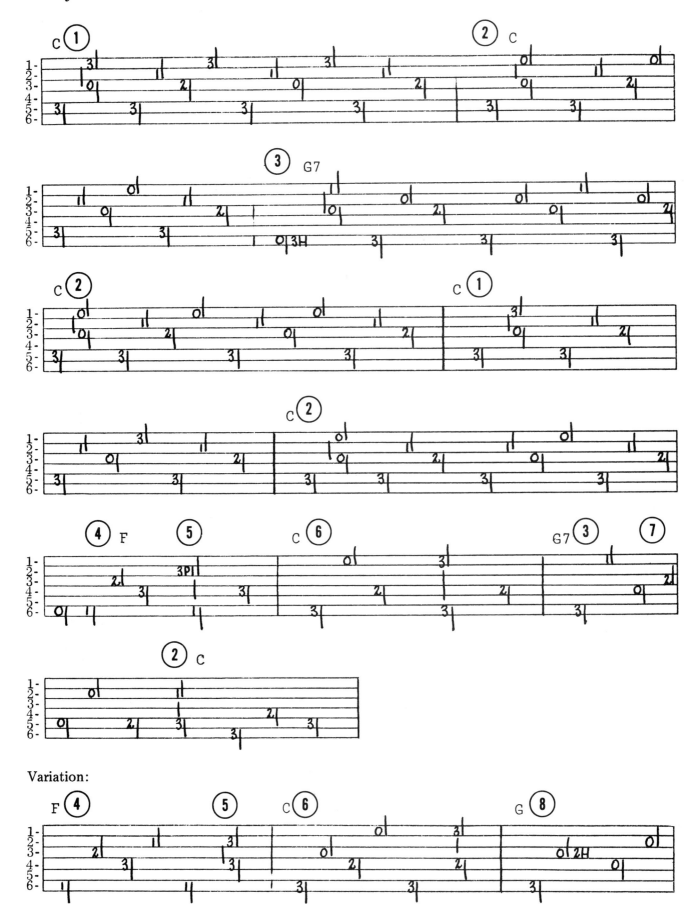

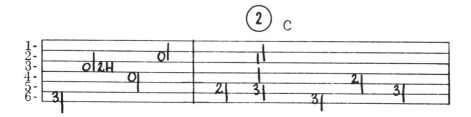

Embellishment:

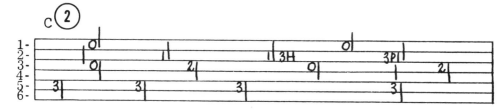

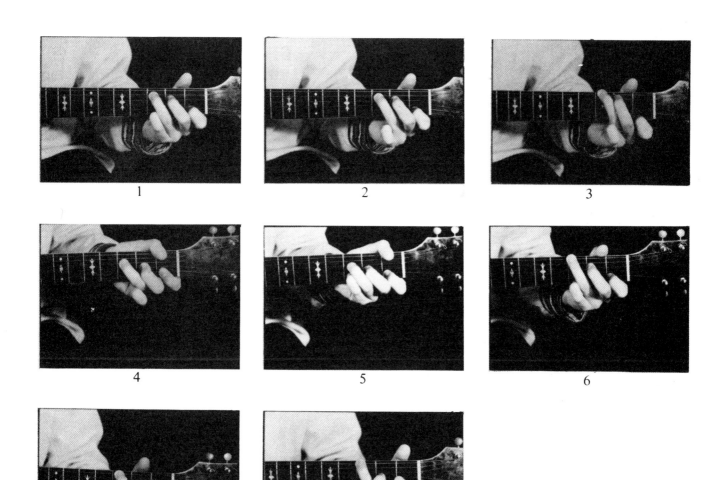

1   2   3

4   5   6

7   8

Candyman

Candyman, been here and gone
Candyman, been here and gone
Candyman, salty dog
If you can't be my candyman,
    you can't be my salty dog

Candyman, candyman
Candyman, fattin' hog
Candyman, Santa Claus
If you can't be my candyman,
    can't be my fattin' hog

Candyman, candyman
Candyman, been here and gone
Candyman, salty dog
I wish I was in New Orleans,
    sitting on the candy stand

Run get the pitcher, get the baby some beer (6X)
I'd give anything in this god almighty world
    to get my candyman home

Candyman, salty dog
Candyman, fattin' hog
Candyman, salty dog
If you can't be my candyman, you can't
    be my man at all

Candyman

Variation:

Embellishment:

Two Step Candyman

Key: C
Section transcribed: The first verse and a variation of the end tag.
Source: Ragtime Guitar—Transatlantic Records in Europe,
   —Kicking Mule Records in the States

The Two Step Candyman will be a challenge for you to master. It is an extremely difficult arrangement. The positions are the same as in the "simple" *Candyman* with the exception of the C chord played in the first part. There is a photograph indicating this position. It might take you some time to build up hand muscles to finger this C chord.

Rev. Davis had many ways of playing *Candyman*. He would tell stories of playing the tune all night at dances and only changing the rhythm. He had a normal version, the two-step, a waltz time version and a duet version (this has been transcribed on the How To Play Blues Guitar l.p.). He also had several versions worked out for the five-string banjo!

In the *Two Step Candyman* the bass pattern is halved during the first part and doubled during the second. The first section reminds me of Skip James' *Special Rider* (transcribed in *Delta Blues Guitar*) in approach to the bass pattern.

One of the hidden tricks of this arrangement appears on the third line of tab as the G⁷ chord is going into a C chord. The last note of the G⁷ lick is the first fret of the second string (a C note) and this gracefully leads in the C chord. Make sure that you don't forget this note!

Two Step Candyman

Rev. Gary Davis (instrumental)

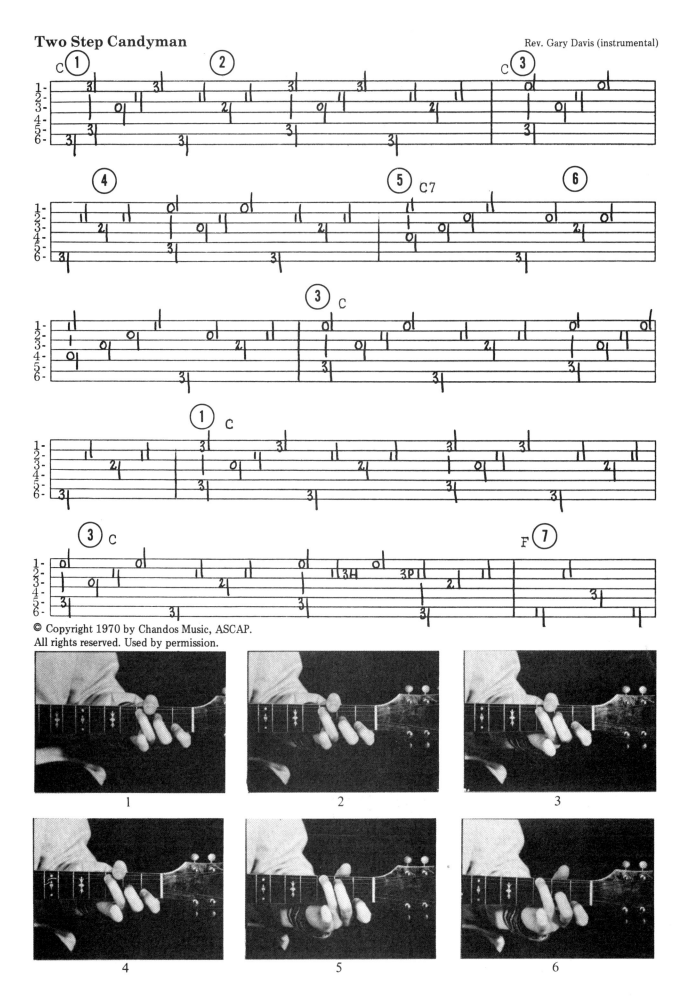

1

2

3

4

5

6

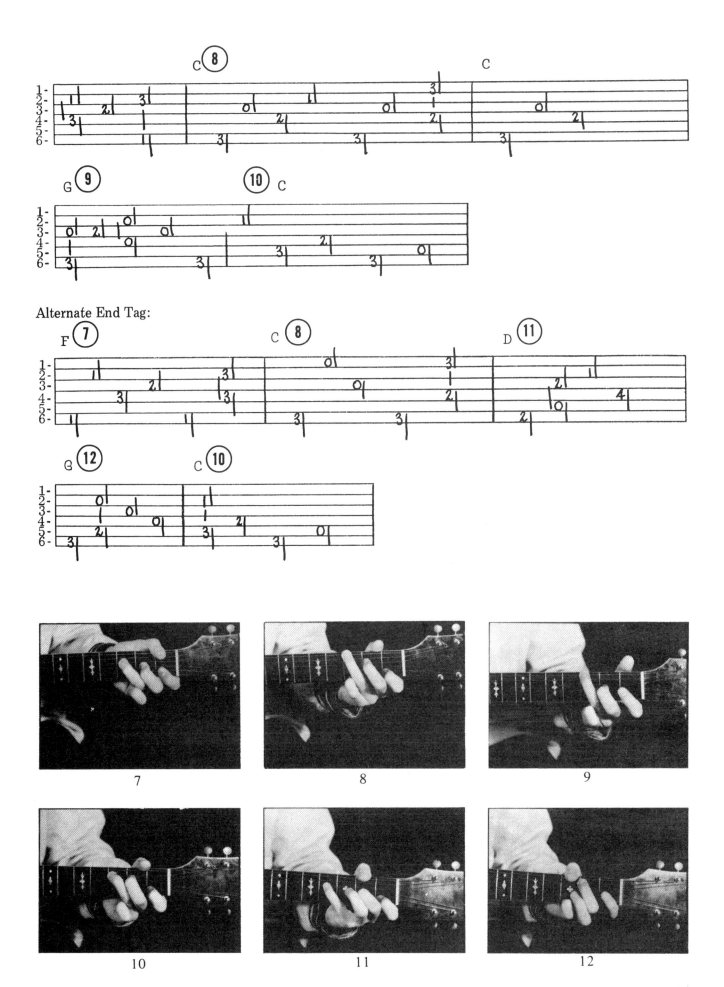

Alternate End Tag:

7

8

9

10

11

12

Two Step Candyman

Alternate end tag:

Goin' To Chattanooga

Key: E
Section transcribed: first verse.
Source: Black Patty Tape Service

Goin' To Chattanooga was sometimes used by Rev. Davis as a first lesson for new students. This always intrigued me as I thought it held several difficult sections to play.

It is a blues in E that can, like *Candyman,* be thought of in two parts. The first section has a halved bass (similar in approach as the *Two Step Candyman*) used while playing the E and A chords. This is an attempt to imitate the old blues piano sound. The second section (which begins half way through the second line of tab) is the turn around end tag, or when the tune goes through an E, F#, B⁷ E progression. This section Rev. Davis would always play differently from verse to verse.

This was a very unusual way of playing in the key of E for Rev. Davis. His other approaches to this key are much more elaborate as you will see when studying *Cross and Evil Woman Blues*.

The arrangement to *Goin' To Chattanooga* somehow reminds me of the playing of Charley Jordan. I suggest you see the Country Blues Guitar and the two Jordan tunes transcribed, i.e. *Keep It Clean* and *Hunkie Tunkie Blues*.

Music by Rev. Gary Davis

Goin' To Chattanooga

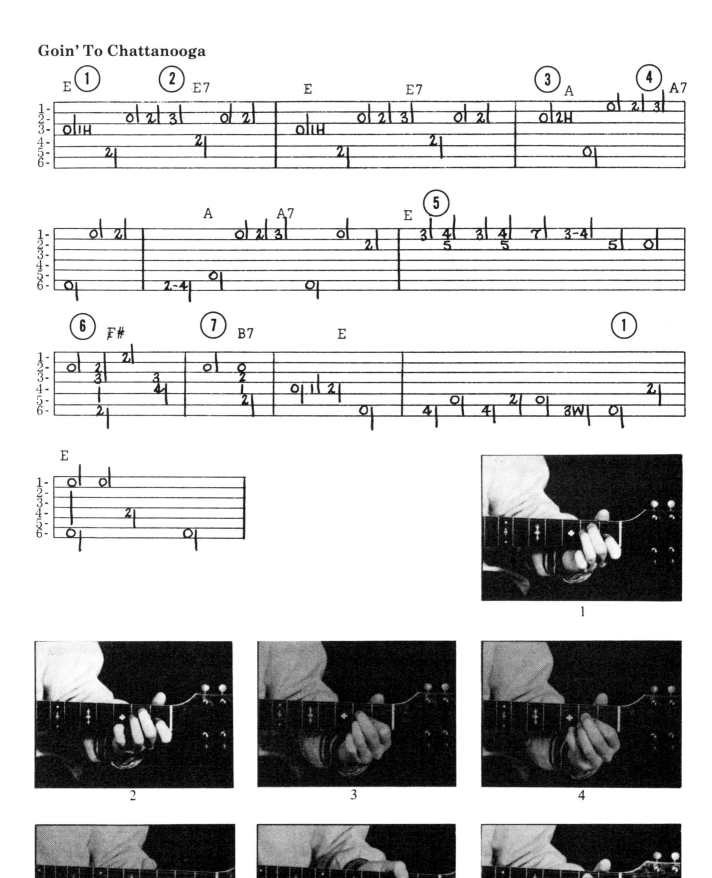

Spoonful

Key: A
Section transcribed: guitar introduction (same as the accompaniment behind the verses)
Source: The Rev. Gary Davis At Newport—Vanguard Records

Almost every bluesman and songster has a version of *Spoonful* in their repertoire. Rev. Davis' arrangement is quite unique in some ways and quite ordinary in others.

All the versions I have heard of this tune are played in the key of A, i.e. Mance Lipscomb's and Howlin' Wolf's. The opening two lines of tab indicate a guitar part that can be heard in other guitarists' versions of *Spoonful.* However, by the third line of tab there appears the "stamp" of Rev. Davis' playing. Here the E[7] section takes on a moving subtle bass line. The fourth line (where the vocal recites "Spoonful" as the guitar imitates this phrasing) is again the usual rendition of this phrase. The fifth line of tab, where we once again go into an E[7] chord presents an interesting variation to this line.

This arrangement should prove enjoyable to play. Perhaps the double timing of the bass in the first two lines might prove tricky but on hearing Rev. Davis' play the tune on record you should discover the right accenting.

The lyrics to this tune are perhaps the most unusual aspect. Rev. Davis has created a version that is quite humorous and different from other sources.

Traditional. Arranged and adapted by Rev. Gary Davis

Spoonful

1

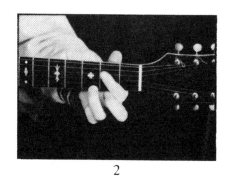

2

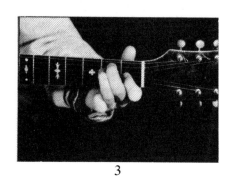

3

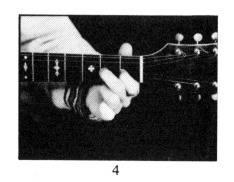

4

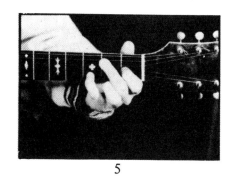

5

6

Spoonful

I come in one morn - ing just 'bout half past ___ four, ___ she

got a chair ___ and knocked me right out the door. ___ She

come to rais - ing sand with me, ___ just 'bout a

spoon - ful, ___ spoon - ful. ___ I nev - er

know such a stir been raised be - fore, ___ just 'bout a

spoon - ful, ___ spoon - ful. ___

I come in one morning just 'bout half past four
She got a chair and knocked me right back out the door
She came to raisin' sand with me, just 'bout a spoonful
I never knew such a stir been raised before, just 'bout a spoonful, spoonful

Come in one morning just about half past nine
She got the biggest chair in the house and tried her best to knock me blind
She was raisin' sand with me again, just 'bout a spoonful
Standing on her head saying, "If you want to get along with me, give me my spoonful"

Come in one night, just about half past ten
Stuck my key in the door and I couldn't get it in
She was on the inside, standing on her head, 'bout a spoonful
She had the whole neighborhood stirred up, just 'bout a spoonful

Come in one evening just to get my dinner
She got so bad on my hands, I told her I had to stick my sword in her
Raisin' so much sand with me, just 'bout a spoonful
Never known such devil raised before in my life, just 'bout a spoonful

I come in one evening, I just got my pay
Throwed my pocketbook in her lap, she threw it back at me and said, "Go your way"
She didn't want no money, she said, "I just want you to give me my spoonful
You ain't going to get along with me until you give me my spoonful"

Come in one evening to go downtown
She got a sewing iron and knocked me down to the ground
Started raisin' sand with me again, 'bout a spoonful
I never known such a cuttin' before 'bout a spoonful

I come in tired one night, hungry and sleepy as I could be
She got a kettle of water and tried to scald the fool out of me
Started that same thing again, just 'bout a spoonful
"If you want to get along with me in this house man, you better give me my spoonful"

Mine All Troubled Blues
(Eagle Rockin' Blues)

Key: A
Section transcribed: A normal verse.
Source: Black Patty Tape Service (for the guitar transcription)
New Blues and Gospel—Biograph Records (for vocal version of *Eagle Rockin' Blues*)

After studying with Rev. Davis for one year I began collecting tapes featuring the old 78's of Blind Boy Fuller, one of Rev. Davis' first students. I came across several recorded tunes that I was sure had originated with Rev. Davis and that Fuller had copied. One of these tunes was *Weepin' Willow Blues.* Somehow, the guitar arrangement had the mark of Rev. Davis' style.

When I mention this to Rev. Davis he chuckled and confirmed my suspicions. He then played his version of the tune.

Mine All Troubled Blues is a beautiful arrangement of a blues in A. The basic motif travels from a minor to a major chord. This gives the song a strong texture as well as a strange "feel." I have transcribed the way Rev. Davis played behind the singing of the verses. The only version I have of him playing this arrangement is an instrumental one. A year before his death Rev. Davis recorded two albums for Biograph Record Company. The first l.p. features some strong playing. The second is very weak and amongst the tunes presented is *Eagle Rocking Blues* which is a vocal version of *Mine All Troubled Blues.* I suggest you hear this only to get an idea how the lyrics can fit with the guitar part. In fact, on this version the guitar playing is very indecisive. To hear the correct guitar playing of this tune I suggest you get the Black Patty Tape.

The lyrics to both of these songs, can easily be sung to the following arrangement.

I suggest you try to hear Fuller's version which can be found on a reissue l.p. *Blind Boy Fuller On Down,* Saydisc 143. Another Fuller arrangement that I thought had Rev. Davis' mark was *Careless Love* and *Corrine, Corrine, What Makes You Treat Me So?* Both tunes use the same guitar playing (I have transcribed *Careless Love* in *Ragtime Blues Guitarist,* Oak).

The blues in A was a favorite of Rev. Davis. A more elaborate arrangement will be studied further on in this book when we come to *I'm Throwin' Up My Hands.*

Words and music by Rev. Gary Davis

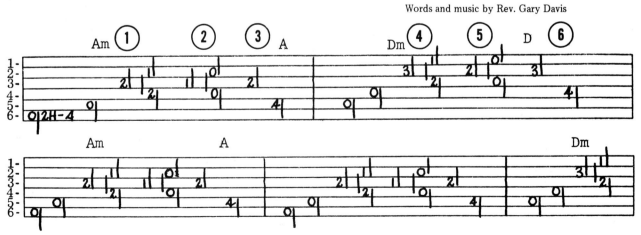

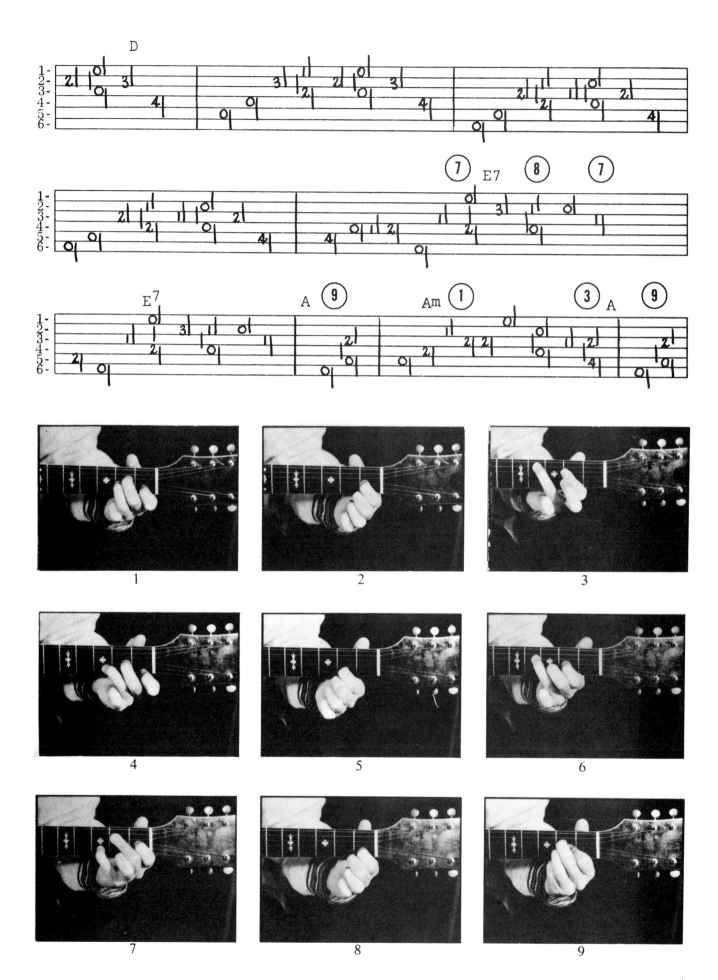

Mine All Troubled Blues (Eagle Rockin' Blues)

Oh, my mind's all troubled, like the waters on the deep blue sea (2X)
Thinking about the gal I love so well, she got so far from me

I'm going to get drunk, tell everything I know (2X)
The girl that I love, she quit me and said she didn't want me no more

From *Weepin' Willow* by Blind Boy Fuller

Lord that weepin' willow and that mournin' dove
That weepin' willow and that mournin' dove
I got a gal up the country, Lord, you know I sure do love

Now, if you see my woman, tell her I says hurry home
You see my woman, tell her I says hurry home
I ain't had no lovin' since my gal been gone

Where it t'ain't no love, ain't no gettin' along
Where it ain't no love, mama, ain't no gettin' along
My gal treat me so mean and dirty, sometime I don't know right from wrong

Lord I lied down last night, tried to take my rest
I lied down last night, tried to take my rest
You know, my mind got to ramblin' just like wild geese in the west

Gonna buy me a bulldog, watch you whilst I sleep
Gonna buy me a bulldog, watch you whilst I sleep
Just to keep these men from makin' this early mornin' creep

Now, if you see my woman, tell her I says hurry home
You see my woman, tell her I says hurry home
I ain't had no lovin' since my little gal been gone

You gonna want my love, baby, some lonesome day
You gonna want my love, mama, some old lonesome day
Then it be too late, I'll be gone too far away

note: This record was originally released as a 78 by the Decca Record
Company—Decca 7881. It can be found on a Saydisc re-issue l.p. of
Blind Boy Fuller's songs.

Reverend Gary Davis— Blues and Gospel

by Stephen Calt

At seventy-five, the Reverend Gary Davis is virtually an institution, his musical reputation so secure that his astonishing feats as a performer are apt to be taken for granted. Despite his advanced age his life has changed little over the past decade; when he is not giving concerts, he is likely to be regaling visitors at his Jamaica, Queens home with stories or musical pointers. No other "folk" musician is more generous with his time and gifts. His five dollar lessons are an outrageous bargain, but Davis is reluctant to hike his prices, reasoning: "I don't never look for a cow to give more milk than what she's made to give...I don't go around everybody's pocket and make myself a bed and go to sleep; I don't think that's right."

Over the years many musicians have lined their own pockets with renditions of Davis pieces. His songs have been recorded by Dave Van Ronk, Taj Mahal, and the Grateful Dead, and his playing has influenced various guitarists with no immediate relationship to his style: Ry Cooder, Stefan Grossman and Larry Johnson. But Davis himself acknowledges no musical mentor, declaring of music: "It's a thing you have to work out yourself. No one else can work it out for you."

He entered the ministry in the 1930's on a similarly independent note. His formal theological training consisted of a single session at a school for the blind near Spartanburg, South Carolina (he attended through the patronage of a white Souuherner who was impressed by his guitar playing). After sampling courses in the Bible, Braille, and organ-playing, his stomach rebelled against the inadequate institutional food offered. On the pulpit as an assistant pastor he continues to shift for himself, never preaching a preconceived text.

Davis' innate optimism and his religious faith have enabled him to rationalize and even surmount setbacks that would have embittered other men. In his own blindness he saw a larger and ultimately benevolent design: "If you got a dog, you know, you don't want him to run around; you know the next thing you do is tie him....Sometimes God has a way of fixin' people so He can get a hand on you....And sometimes you know when God takes a man's sight He gives 'em somethin' greater."

He refuses to speculate on whether he would have taken up music had he not been blind from birth or childhood (accounts on his tragedy vary). Besides providing a livelihood and an outlet for his huge creative gifts, music came to gratify his competitive instincts. He recalls his early progress as swift and sure, adding: "I never was shy of no guitar players." By the 1920's he proudly bracketed himself among South Carolina's elite guitarists, who included his blind acquaintances Willie Walker of Greenville ("He was a guitar dog") and Simmie Dooley of Spartanburg. Both were recorded years before Davis.

A prince of his profession, Davis was treated like a lackey when he made his debut for the American Record Company (ARC) in 1935. Discovered by a Burlington, North Carolina storekeeper named J. B. Long, he was persuaded to make his first journey north on the grounds that it was primarily "a pleasure trip through the country." He received less for his pains than his colleagues Bull City Red and Blind Boy Fuller, a Winston-Salem protege he had met earlier in

1935 when Fuller's wife Cora came to Durham in search of her errant husband. Long, Davis recalls, "paid the other boys off but wanted me to wait for mine." After a belated and hardly equitable pay-off (about $40 for 14 sides), he never saw Long again.

Davis was neither jealous of Fuller's greater commercial success nor apt to pull rank on a man whose repertoire he had largely developed. Though he was admittedly "a very poor hand" for socializing, his friendly relationship with Fuller survived the latter's apathy towards his religious discourse. Even today, Davis refuses to pass the kind of doctrinaire judgements on blues so typical of the regenerate bluesmen, remarking simply: "Everything that people say is a sin is not a sin." Despite his Baptist affiliations he is essentially non-denominational in spirit and stresses the subjective aspects of his sacred music: "It's just what you let it be. It means just as much to me as it does to you. Perhaps it might mean more to me...and that's what required me to go further with it."

Although Davis' equivocal rejection of blues material pained early blues critics, who melodramatically attributed it to his blindness, his fondness for spirituals long pre-dated his conversion. "I played 'em in childhood 'cause my grandmother loved to hear 'em," he recalls. His own ministry was never opportunistic by nature and he barely supported himself with three small churches he founded near Durham, the largest of which attained a total of twenty-eight members. "Nobody could say I married him for his money," his wife Annie remarks, " 'cause really and truly he had no money." A devout church-goer, she squelches Davis' minor lapses from rectitude, recruits his guests for revivals and (with the Reverend) looks forward to the early re-opening of his church, which folded over three years ago following the death of its pastor.

Shortly after marrying The Reverend during the Second World War, his wife obtained a position as a cook with a family in Mamaroneck, N.Y. She arranged for the Traveler's Aid Society to bring him up from Durham, a move he contemplated with some anxiety. "I had never heard nothin' good about New York 'fore I came up here," he says. Once the Davis' moved to 169th Street in the south Bronx around 1944 he began playing for street audiences, "not so much that I liked it but that's the best I could do." He was lionized by the annotators of his first LP's as a "street minstrel" but notes himself: "I was glad to get away from it (street singing) 'cause there's too many different kinds of people you meet up with in the street, and it's not recognized too....They call it beggin'; pan-handlin'."

A more satisfactory avenue of employment emerged through the guitar lessons Davis had given informally "ever since I started out playin'." Without advertising ("I let myself be the sign") he attracted a number of fans as students. Yet during the "folk revival" of the Forties and Fifties he received little publicity by comparison with far lesser guitarists of the Josh White and Brownie McGee ilk. He was content to bide his time, feeling that, "it don't take one match to set the world afire." His torch song proved to be *Samson and Delilah;* with the royalties from Peter, Paul and Mary's pop version of the piece he was able to purchase his own home in Jamaica about seven years ago.*

*This article was written in 1971, a year before Rev. Davis passed away.

Baby, Let Me Lay It On You

Key: G
Section transcribed: Guitar introduction (identical to the guitar part played behind the vocal).
*Source: Lo' I Be With You Always—*Kicking Mule Records

This is another popular arrangement of Rev. Davis'. Both Blind Boy Fuller and Bob Dylan have recorded this version. In many ways the guitar playing reminds me of Memphis Minnie's *Where's My Good Man* (transcribed in the *Country Blues Guitar,* Oak).

This song presents us with some interesting combinations of styles and techniques. In fact, it is from here on that our study will become more complex. The tune begins with a normal alternating bass pattern. By the end of the first line we are picking individual runs that deviate from the bass pattern and break up the alternating bass texture. The second line of tab introduces three interesting and unique chord positions. Rev. Davis had a strange manner in fingering certain chords. I always wondered why and how he managed these types of fingerings. I finally discovered the answer when learning that his left hand wrist had been broken and when it set it set in a distorted manner so that it was somewhat left of the axis of the left hand. This enabled him to attack the fingerboard in a manner much different than a normal guitarist. The result was a host of chord positions using the thumb wrapped around the neck of the guitar or having the index finger grabbing notes that were usually too hard to hold down. Naturally, these positions will take some getting used to and you will have to develop strong hands. But they are essential in getting the proper sound.

There is a complete version (both guitar playing and vocal) of this song on the *Lo' I Be With You Always* album. There are also various instrumental versions on l.p.'s but these are not played as well or as decisively as on the Kicking Mule disc.

Baby, Let Me Lay It On You

Words and music by Rev. Gary Davis

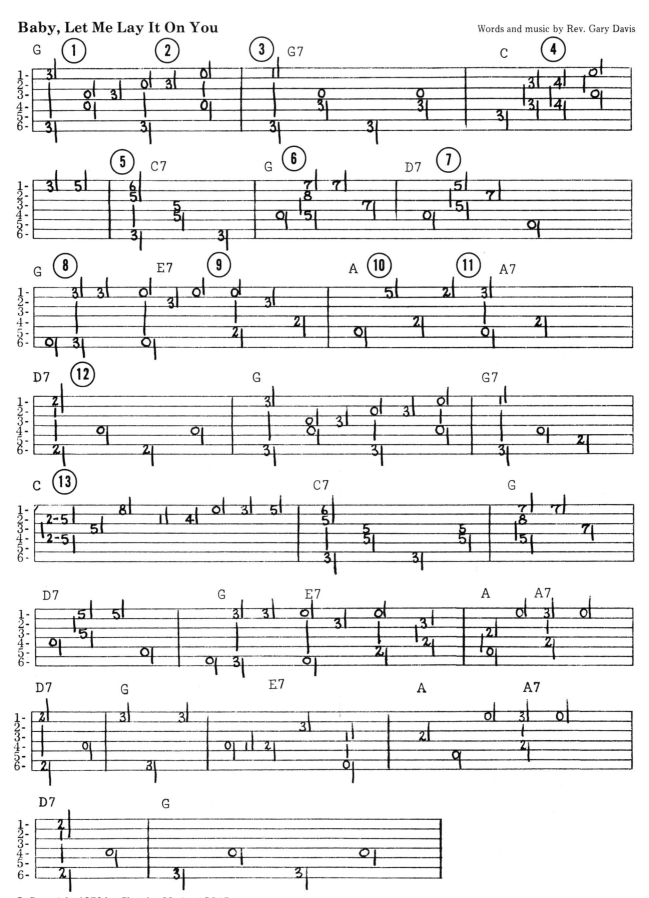

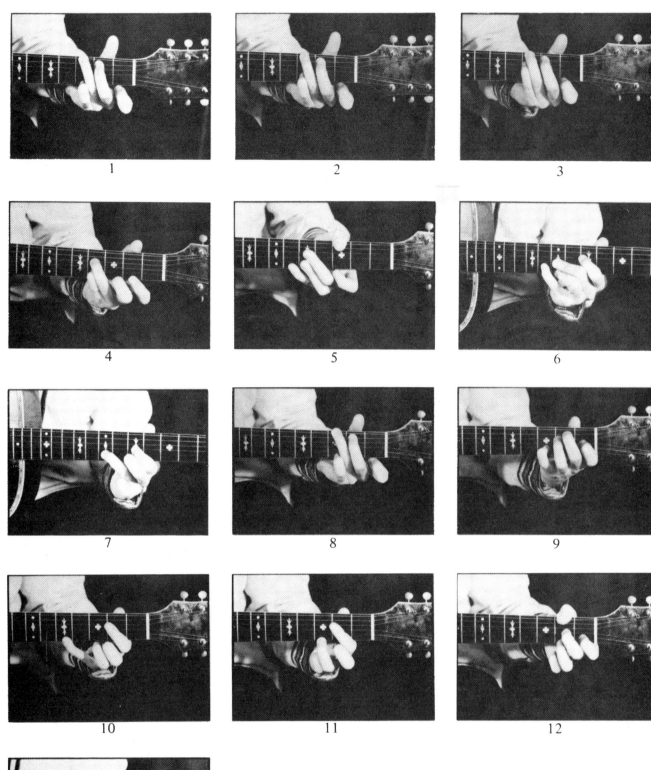

1   2   3

4   5   6

7   8   9

10   11   12

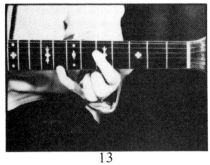

13

Baby, Let Me Lay It On You

Baby, let me lay it on you. Baby, let me lay it on you.
I'd give you everything in this God almighty world, if you just let me lay it on you.
Please sugar, let me lay it on you. Please m'am! let me lay it on you.
I'd give you everything in this God almighty world, if you just let me lay it on you.
Please m'am, let me lay it on you.

I'd buy you a brand new car; buy you a motorcycle on the side.
I'd give you everything in a God almighty world, just let me lay it on you, please.
Please sugar I'd buy you a Greyhound bus, and give you a nice jet plane
I'd tell you what I'll do, I'll run behind, here's $1000, let me lay it on you, any jet complaints?
 let me lay it on you, cadillac and a motorcycle, let me lay it on you

Baby, Let Me Lay It On You

She's Funny That Way

Key: G
Section transcribed: Guitar introduction and the first verse.
Source: Blues and Gospel—Biograph Records

Lo' I Be With You Always—Kicking Mule Records

This is our first ragtime song. The guitar part is not difficult and you should have no problems in mastering it. The only difficult phrase might be found on the third line of tablature where there is a rapid change of chords, i.e. G, G^7, C, $E\flat^7$.

This was one of Rev. Davis' most popular performing tunes. It was also recorded in the 1930's by Blind Boy Fuller.

The ragtime progression of G, E^7, A^7, D^7 and G can be found in many tunes. It is the basis for the song *Salty Dog* as well as other more complex Rev. Davis instrumentals. *Twelve Sticks,* another Davis number, takes this progression and explores the many rhythmic possibilities. This tune will be studied in the next Rev. Davis volume.

Rev. Davis usually ended up this tune by playing the piece in double time. This gives the song a real ragtime quality and can be a challenge for you to play.

She's Funny That Way

Words and music by Rev. Gary Davis

Guitar Introduction:

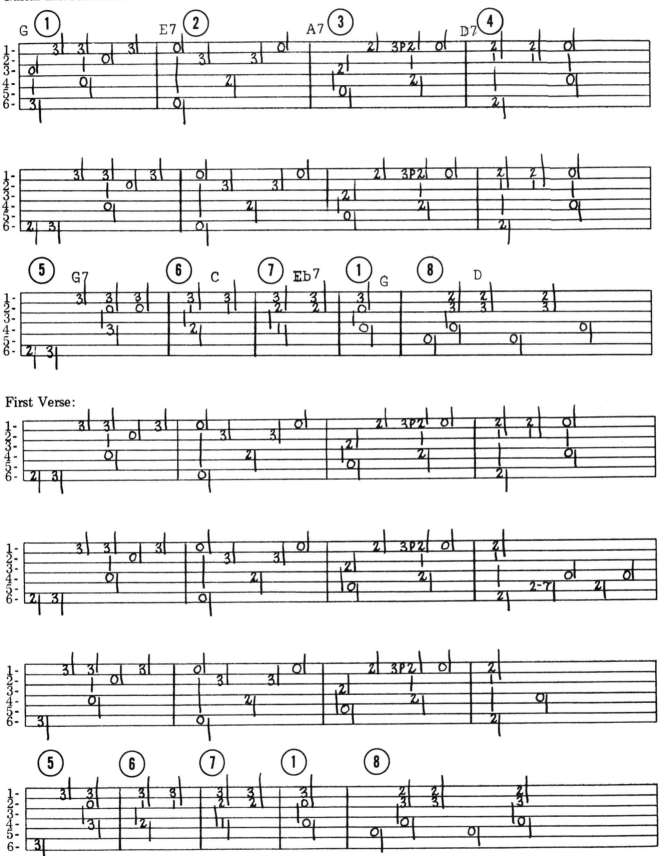

First Verse:

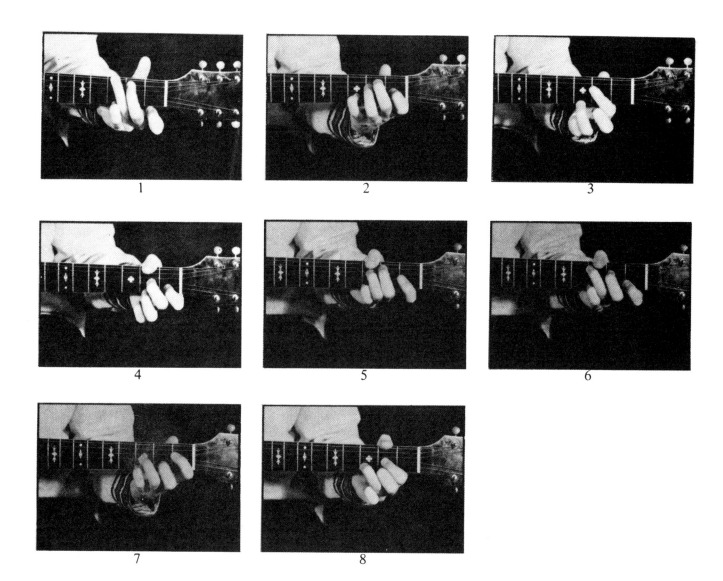

1

2

3

4

5

6

7

8

She's Funny That Way

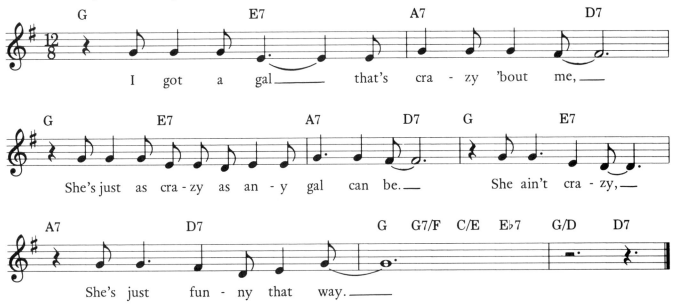

I got a gal that's crazy 'bout me
She's just as crazy as any gal can be
She ain't crazy, she's just funny that way

One thing 'bout this gal I can't understand
I found out she's just a fool 'bout one old man
She ain't crazy, she's just funny that way

She got to the place that she don't like no women friends
She don't want no woman be shifting around taking her man in
She ain't crazy, she's just funny that way

Now, some people say this gal is just tight like that
But when she calls her man she always wants him to be right there
She ain't crazy, she's just funny that way

I found out this gal is just as jealous as any gal can be
She ain't satisfied when her man is right around her knee
She ain't crazy, she's just funny that way

This gal will work hard for you every day and buy your clothes and shoes
Come in and look for you and can't find you, she'll begin to have the blues
She ain't crazy, she's just funny that way

note:

On the Kicking Mule double l.p.—Lo' I Be With You Always there is another version of She's Funny That Way where Rev. Davis performs the tune on a six string banjo. This version captures much more of the spirit of the song than the Biograph version. There are several slight changes in the lyrics, especially the last line to each verse. Here Rev. Davis changes the line to read—*I found out she's not crazy, she's just funny that way!* or *She's not crazy, I found out she's just crazy that way.* **The over-all effect is much more poignant and humorous. I have transcribed several additional verses that appear on this l.p. that are not included above:**

I found out she's a one man woman, wants to treat her man right.
And if she ever catch you crooked boy, you'll have this gal to fight
I found out she's not crazy, she's just funny that way.

She's nice and kind, she's quiet as a mouse
And she don't want you to be running around, slippin' to no other woman's house
She ain't crazy, she's just funny that way

Now man, if you tangle up with a gal like this, you better be sure you know what you're doing
'Cause there's plenty about this gal, find enough for any young man to learn
She's not crazy, I found out she's funny that way

She's a nice country girl, she never been to no college, no man's school
But she'll let every man that she has know that she ain't nobody's fool
She ain't crazy, she's just funny that way

Before she'll go to her job she'll come to her bed and kiss you boy, leave you layin' in bed
Come back five o'clock in the evening, look for you and can't find you, she'll go plum out of her head
She ain't crazy, she's just funny that way

First Verse:

Save Up Your Money, John D. Rockerfeller Put The Panic On

Key: C

Section transcribed: I have transcribed two versions. The first was taught to me personally by Rev. Davis. In this version I have also indicated an alternate beginning phrase. The second version is taken from a tape of Rev. Davis where he played the tune in a slightly different fashion.

Source: The first version can be heard on *How To Play Blues Guitar.*

The second version from Black Patty Tape Service.

With *Save Up Your Money,* I would like to begin a study of various blues and ragtime techniques in the key of C. This was one of Rev. Davis' most preferred keys to play in. He had arranged many blues, rags as well as religious numbers in this key and we can learn a great deal about his approach to playing by studying the various songs that follow.

Save Up Your Money, John D. Rockerfeller Put The Panic On is an old carnival show song. It is in the tradition of *Candyman* though it is played in a much more varied fashion. In this tune we are essentially playing the melody and around that we are embroidering it with rhythmic licks and treble runs. The only section that remains constant can be found in the middle of the second line of tab. Here we pick a melody out while holding down a C chord.

The first transcribed section is one that I wrote down directly after Rev. Davis taught me the piece. I have indicated the basic structure as well as one variation for the first line (until the line reaches the F chord section). I have recorded this version on my *How To Play Blues Guitar* l.p.

The second transcribed version is taken from another performance of Rev. Davis that I discovered recently. This version offers some interesting variations. You should hear the Black Patty Tape of this version as it is interesting to hear how Rev. Davis could play the song for five minutes or so, and never repeat a phrase. Each verse would take the song deeper into variations. It was, in many ways, the same experience you can have when hearing jazz musicians improvise on a theme. Rev. Davis loved to sit on his favorite worn-out chair and play this type of number all into the afternoon and evening.

I was never able to get Rev. Davis to sing the words to the guitar arrangement. The best that he did was to offer two verses:

Save up your money, don't buy no corn,
John D. Rockerfeller put the panic on.

The gal I'm lovin' she's long and tall,
She got something make a panther squall.

The approach presented in this tune will be explored one step further in our next selection: *Sally, Where'd You'd Get Your Liquor From.*

Save Up Your Money, John D. Rockerfeller Put The Panic On

Traditional. Arranged and
adapted by Rev. Gary Davis

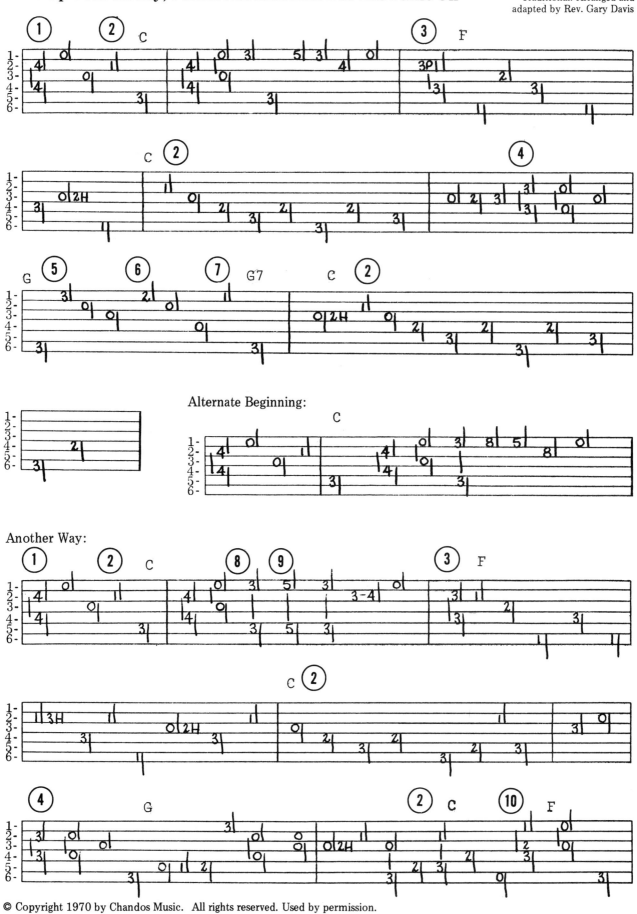

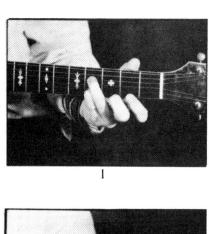

1

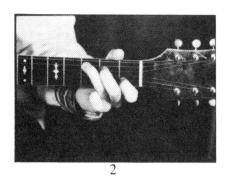

2

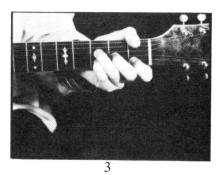

3

4

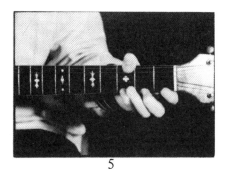

5

6

7

8

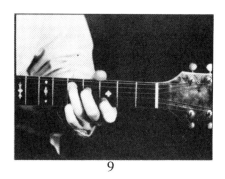

9

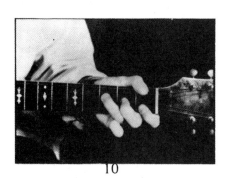

10

Save Up Your Money, John D. Rockerfeller Put The Panic On

Alternate beginning:

Another way:

Sally, Where'd You Get Your Liquor From?

Key: C
Section transcribed: Guitar part to be played with verse and chorus.
Source: Blues and Gospel—Biograph Records Black Patty Tape Service.

This is another carnival show song. The lyrics almost approach the absurd. Rev. Davis loved to entertain people with this tune. As a guitar arrangement it offers many challenges. It follows through on the lessons learned in *Save Up Your Money* but adds more ingredients. There are vamps on chords (where we are basically just strumming a chord) which are followed by treble runs that lead right up to our middle register (this is seen on the end of the first line of tab where the run begins on the fifth fret of the first string and ends up at the second fret fourth string).

The chorus section is more difficult to master than the verse. In fact, this section is very similar to several arrangements Rev. Davis created for religious numbers, i.e. *I Belong To The Band, Pure Religion.*

Another interesting aspect is found on the eighth line of tab. Here we have an identical chord change as appeared in *She's Funny That Way* but naturally here it is transposed to the key of C. This part might be a challenge to finger as your left hand index finger will have to bar the first four strings while your other fingers reach out for chord formations!

Words and music by Rev. Gary Davis

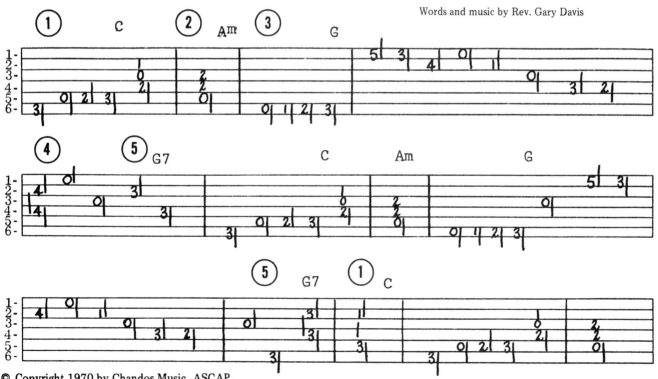

Sally, Where'd You Get Your Liquor From

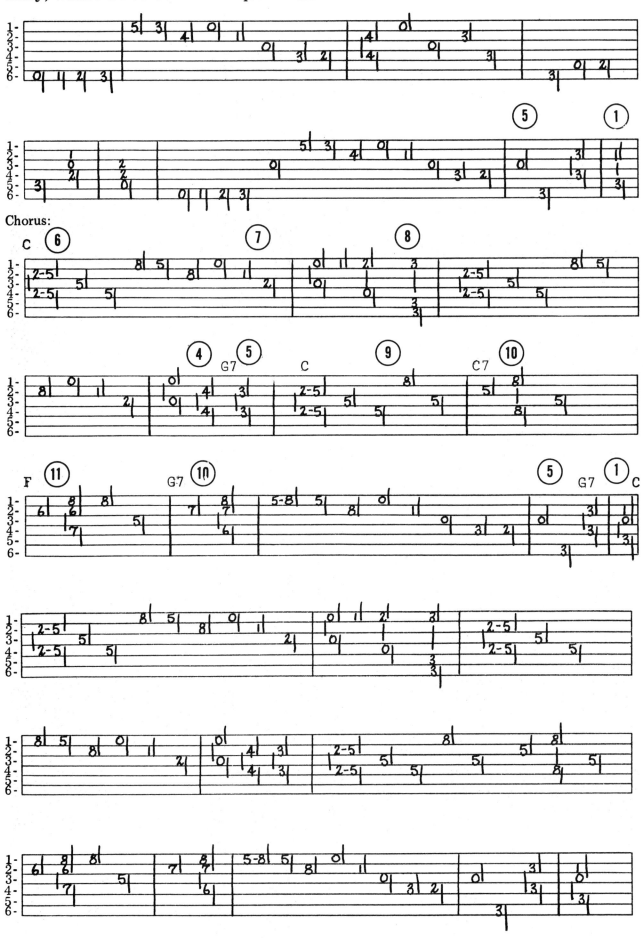

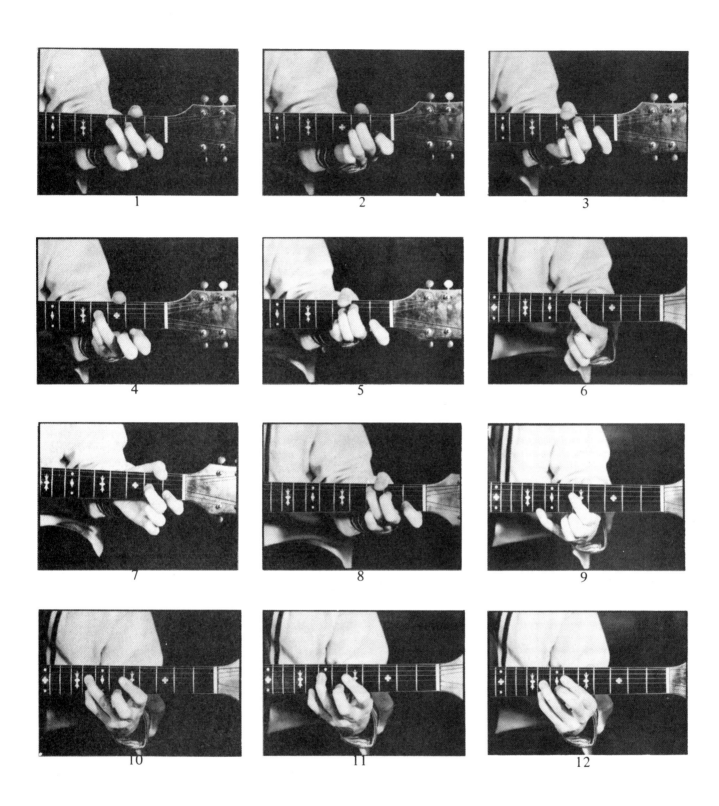

Sally, Where'd You Get Your Liquor From

84

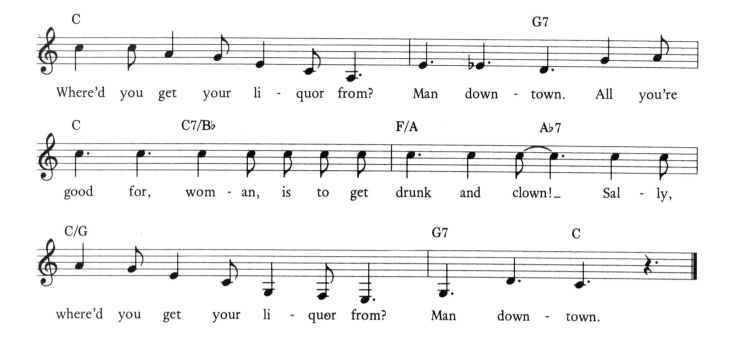

Where'd you get your li-quor from? Man down-town. All you're good for, wom-an, is to get drunk and clown! Sal-ly, where'd you get your li-quor from? Man down-town.

Old man Peter was a mighty man
    Where'd you get your liquor from? Man downtown
Combed his head in a frying pan
    Where'd you get your liquor from? Man downtown
Washed his face in a wagon wheel
    Where'd you get your liquor from? Man downtown
Died with a toothache in his heel
    Where'd you get your liquor from? Man downtown

Chorus (2x):
Sally, where'd you get your liquor from? Man downtown
Sally, where'd you get your liquor from? Man downtown
All you're good for, woman, is to get drunk and clown
Sally, where'd you get your liquor from? Man downtown

Sally you just ain't no doggone good
    Where'd you get your liquor from? Man downtown
I would get rid of you Sally, if I could
    Where'd you get your liquor from? Man downtown
The old mule kicked, the old cow pranced
    Where'd you get your liquor from? Man downtown
Old sow whistled while the little pig danced
    Where'd you get your liquor from? Man downtown

I come in one evening about half past four
    Where'd you get your liquor from? Man downtown
Sally done got all of my food and strown it all over the floor
    Where'd you get your liquor from? Man downtown
There's one thing Sally I'm just going to do
    Where'd you get your liquor from? Man downtown
I'm going to get me a woman treat me better than you
    Where'd you get your liquor from? Man downtown

Sally went up on the hill with a glass in her hand
    Where'd you get your liquor from? Man downtown
Trying to find another drunk so she can come back
    and raise some more sand
    Where'd you get your liquor from? Man downtown

You ain't worth the salt that goes in your bread
    Where'd you get your liquor from? Man downtown
Ain't worth a pound of lead takes to keep you dead
    Where'd you get your liquor from? Man downtown
One of these days I'll tell you what I'm going to do
    Where'd you get your liquor from? Man downtown
I'm going to get me another woman to do right and get rid of you
    Where'd you get your liquor from? Man downtown

Never seen a bottle like this before
    Where'd you get your liquor from? Man downtown
He baptised a bullfrog in '54
    Where'd you get your liquor from? Man downtown
I would get your liquor just any old day
    Where'd you get your liquor from? Man downtown
These good looking women don't let me pray
    Where'd you get your liquor from? Man downtown

Old mule and old cow pranced
    Where'd you get your liquor from? Man downtown
Old sow whistled while the little pig danced
    Where'd you get your liquor from? Man downtown
Bullfrog jumped on the pulpit stand
    Where'd you get your liquor from? Man downtown
He preached the gospel like a natural man
    Where'd you get your liquor from? Man downtown

Sally, Where'd You Get Your Liquor From

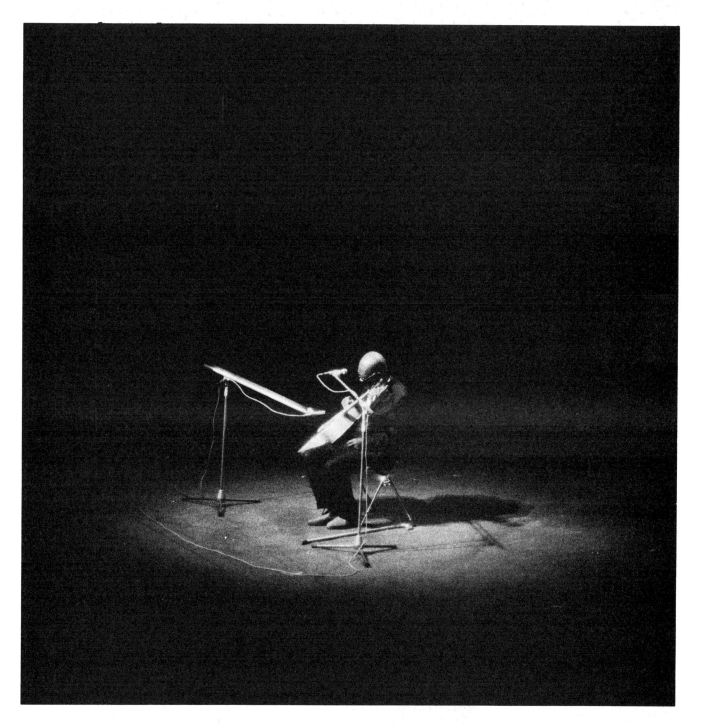

Hesitation Blues

Key: C
Section transcribed: First guitar break (similar to the guitar part played with
  each verse).
Source: Lo' I Be With You Always—Kicking Mule Records.

Hesitation Blues is one of the most widely sung blues. Rev. Davis' version
presents a beautiful and intricate guitar arrangement. His way of playing the tune
has been used by many of todays musicians, i.e. Hot Tuna and Ralph McTell.

There are several recorded versions of this arrangement but the most definitive can be found on the *Lo' I Be With You Always* album. Here Rev. Davis
really goes to town. It is a performance lasting over ten minutes that has a basic
guitar structure. Over this we have over 24 verses that give us every possible
lyrical variation needed.

I have transcribed the first guitar break. This is basically what is played
behind each verse though Rev. Davis naturally changes runs and rhythmic tex-
tures from verse to verse. On other recordings of *Hesitation Blues,* i.e. 77
Records, you can hear Rev. Davis take a different approach to playing this
tune. There he plays it in the fashion of *Save Up Your Money* where there is a
loosely knit verse structure that is heavily improvised upon. I suggest you attempt that way after the version I have transcribed has been mastered.

The guitar part written out is a beautiful jig-saw puzzle. Each run flows into
each section creating a wonderful guitar arrangement.

The fourth line of tablature presents another way of playing the end tag C, C⁷,
F, A$^{\flat 7}$, C, differently than played in *Sally, Where'd You Get Your Liquor From?*

Traditional. Arranged and adapted by Rev. Gary Davis

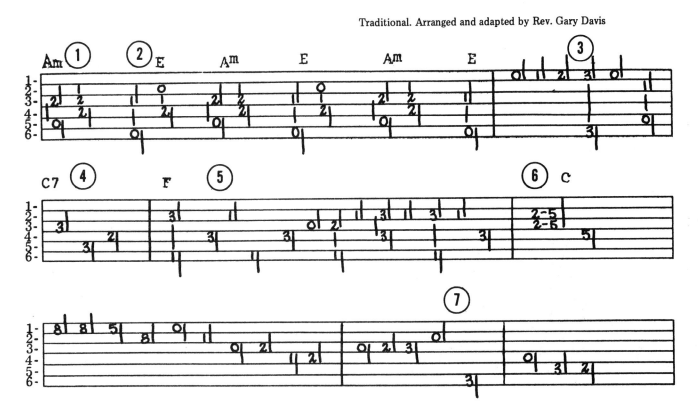

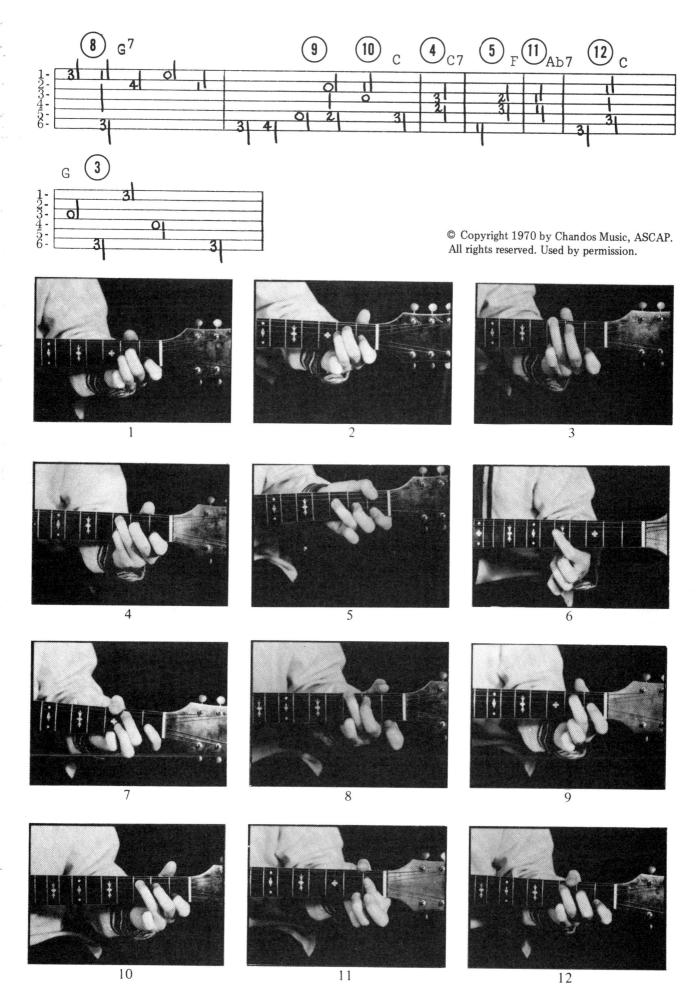

1

2

3

4

5

6

7

8

9

10

11

12

Hesitation Blues

I woke up this morning just 'bout half past four
Hesitation blues was knocking on my door

Refrain:
Tell me, how long, do I baby, have to wait
Can I let you know? Why must I hesitate ?

Ain't no use in me working so hard
I got me two good women
    working in the rich folks' yard

I ain't your good man, ain't your good man's son
But I can get in the place of your good man,
    'til your good man comes

Well, I ain't no miller, ain't no miller's son
But I can grind a little corn,
    'til the miller comes

I ain't no wine presser,
    ain't no wine presser's son
But I can press out a little juice for you,
    'til the wine presser comes

I ain't no grocery man,
    ain't no grocery man's son
But I can buy you a little groceries,
    'til the grocery man comes

I ain't no cradle rocker,
    ain't no cradle rocker's son
But I can do a little rockin' for you,
    'til the rocker man comes

Well, I ain't no doctor, ain't no doctor's son
But I can cure a few cases, 'til the doctor comes

Eagle on the dollar say, "In God We Trust"
Woman flashy, wants a man but I declare
    she wants a dollar first

I ain't no bookkeeper,
    ain't no bookkeeper's son
But I can keep a few books,
    'til the bookkeeper comes

I ain't no milkman, ain't no milkman's son
But I can keep you supplied,
    'til your milkman comes

I ain't no chauffeur, ain't no chauffeur's son
But I can do a little driving,
    'til your chauffeur comes

Well, I ain't no back-breaker,
   ain't no back-breaker's son
But I can stretch out my back,
   'til your back-breaker comes

I ain't got no woman and I ain't got no kid
Ain't got no daughter to be bothered with

I ain't no rent payer, ain't no rent payer's son
But I can scrape up a few rents,
   'til the rent payer comes

Well, I ain't been to heaven but I've been told
St. Peter learnt the angels how to do
   the Jelly Roll

Me and my buddy and two or three more
We get good women everywhere we go

Well, I hitched up the mule and the mule
   wouldn't pull
Took the hunches off the mule and put the
   hunches on the bull

Blacker the berry the sweeter the juice
I'd be a fool if I quit the woman I got
   because it ain't no use

I got hesitating stockings, hesitating shoes
I got a hesitating woman singing me
   the hesitating blues

My good gal quit me, I ain't going to wear no
   black
I always got something to make her
   come running back

Men in the country hollering, "Whoa, haw, gee!"*
Women in the city flying around asking
   the question, "Who wants me?"

Ashes to ashes and dust to dust
Just show me a woman that a man can trust

You know, my mother told me
   when I was just six years old
I'm going to be a good women getter,
   God bless your soul

Additional verses from
Blues and Gospel, Biograph 12030

I was standing on the corner one morning,
   with a dollar in my hand
I was looking for the first woman
   who didn't have no man

I got hesitating shoes and hesitating stockings
I got me a good hesitating woman
   to do my hesitating rockin'

I ain't no preacher, ain't no preacher's son
But I can preach a few sermons,
   'til the preacher comes

I was out on my wagon trying to sell some coal
My gal was slipping around the corner,
   doing her best to sell some jellyrolls

Additional verses from a performance at the
Golden Vanity Folk Club, Boston, Mass. 1959)

I was raised in the country, you know,
   I was born in town
I got elgin movement from my hips on down

The river was all muddy and the pond all dried
Wasn't for these women folk, these men would die

Nickel is a nickel, dime is a dime
A woman says she gets tired of one doggone man
   all the time

Apples on the table, the peaches on the chair
I got to go somewhere to get me a woman,
   'cause I'm tired of sleeping by myself

Whoa, haw, gee means: "stop, go toward the left, go toward the right."

Hesitation Blues

Walkin' Dog Blues

Key: C
Section transcribed: First and second verses.
Source: Ragtime Guitar—Transatlantic Records in Europe.
  —Kicking Mule Records in the States.

Rev. Davis would always introduce *Walkin' Dog Blues* by saying, "Here's the way they used to play that old piano." The guitar arrangement that he developed for this tune gives the impression of a piano though the approach is definitely that of a guitarist. (This is an interesting point as the book Contemporary Ragtime Guitar shows another approach for arranging piano sounds onto the guitar. There the guitar tries to play all the notes that a piano would play. Rev. Davis' piano sounds were taken by having the 'spirit and feel' of the piano transposed onto the guitar.)

This is a rather difficult piece. It combines all the lessons learned in the previous three songs as well as adding a basic phrase that gives the impresison of a counter-point line as played by the left hand of a piano player. This is found on the first line of tab as well as when the tune goes into the F section.

This was the type of piece that Rev. Davis would play a new variation for every verse. The version presented on *Ragtime Guitar* is a good example of that approach.

Walkin' Dog Blues

Music by Rev. Gary Davis

First Verse:

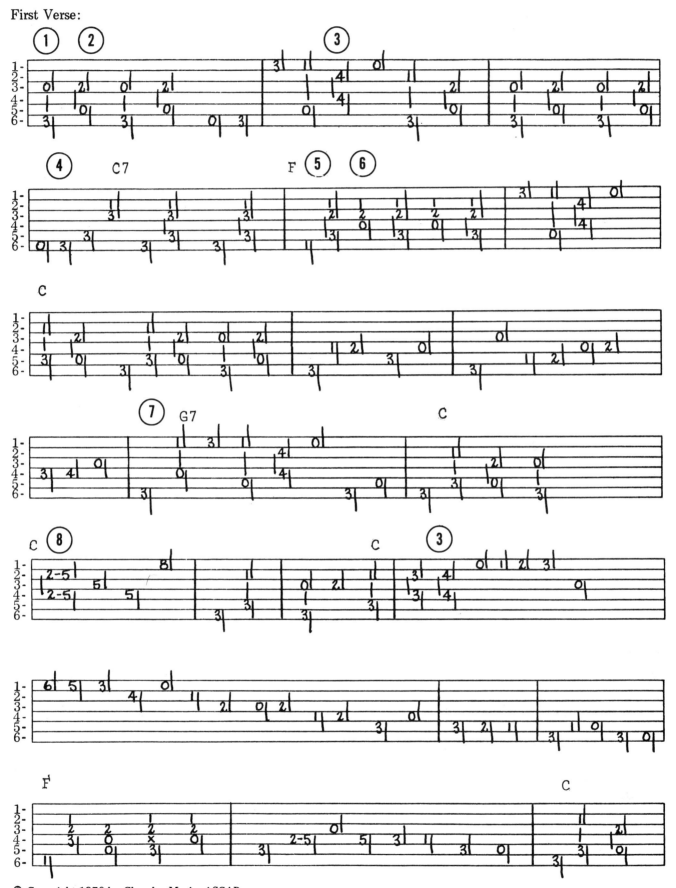

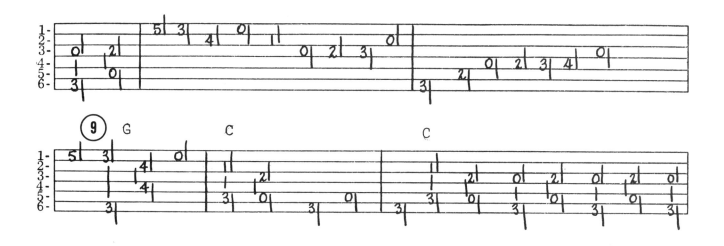

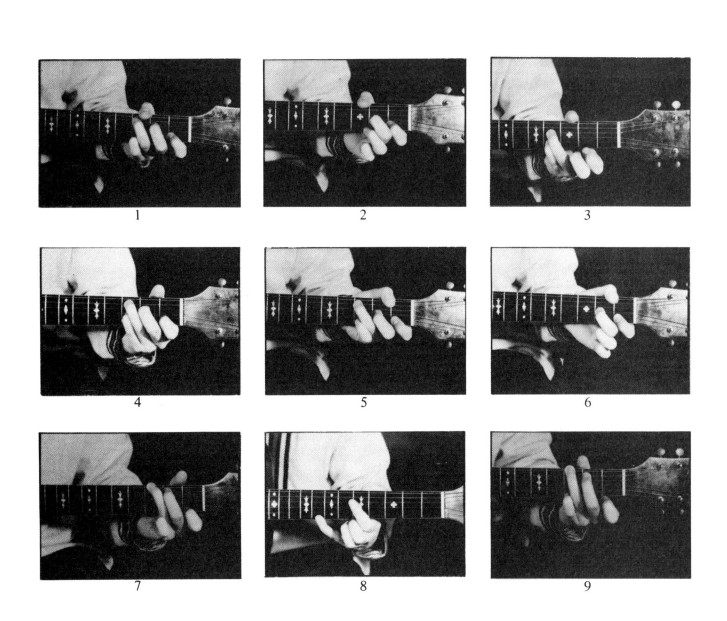

Walkin' Dog Blues

First verse:

96

Reverend Gary Davis

by Sam Charters

What was I thinking about the last time I drove Gary Davis back to his small house behind a grimy apartment building in the Bronx? I try to remember. The weather? the car? traffic? If there was something I've forgotten it. But Gary? It's difficult to forget him. It was sunset, a late spring afternoon. The last red-orange light was filling the sky and the clouds seemed to hang in a slow sadness over New York. I had rolled the windows down and the smells of the spring day filled the car, the wind from the trees and fields of Long Island drifting across the East River tides toward New York. Despite his blindness Gary was looking off toward the river, feeling the warmth in the shifting air and smelling the new grass and the wet earth and the first spring flowers. "I never would come in when it was a day like this and I was young..." He talked as I drove. Not to me—though he'd turn his head toward me when he wanted to emphasize something—but to himself. It was a spring day and he was thinking of other spring days when he had been a small boy and he spent the last light of the afternoons sitting by himself on the sun warmed earth or walking on the country dirt roads back to the farm where he'd been raised. "...My granny could take left over corn pone and make bread out of it again. That's something that people don't have idea of now. She'd let the end piece of the bread get dry, you understand, and then she'd put all those end pieces into a pan with some bacon grease or lard or something like that and she'd cook the two of them together until that old bread was just as soft as it'd been when it was fresh baked..."

Gary is in his seventies now, and it's somehow intimidating; even while it's in a way, meaningless. For an artist's age only has a meaning to his art. If what he's created is still living then he lives with it. The art is himself, and he is his art. It could be this incongruity that's intimidating. Gary has in his music the warmth and the sounds and the smells of a summer day, and he's entering into his life's lingering autumn. It's even more disconcerting because his art is a performer's art.

He doesn't write his music down on paper. His art is in his fingers and his voice; it's the completely personal expression of Gary himself, and even in his seventies he is still so vitally alive that his art is still broadening and deepening. As we drove that spring day he was thinking back to his childhood in Lawrence County, South Carolina, to 1903, to 1905, to 1910, and 1911, but it was as much a part of the present to him as the fading afternoon light was to me.

When we got back to his house he was still talking. There had been heavy rains the day before and the walkway to his house was flooded. A drain had clogged, and four or five inches of muddy water had backed up over the pavement. As we made our way over an improvised path of soaked boards and parts of an old iron stove he kept putting his cane down in the water and laughing, while I was too concerned about keeping my feet out of the water to do much more than say unpleasant things about the owner of the building. Then in the house he sat down in an old stuffed chair and started to play a harmonica that he'd found in a pocket of his coat. "You never have heard me play this piece have you..."

Gary's life is easily sketched, even though the sketch doesn't tell much about the development of his art. He was born April 30, 1896—it may have been another date since he's given other dates at different times that he's been asked—but it was probably in the spring of 1896 on a small farm in the north central hill lands of South Carolina. As he remembered it was so lonely "...you couldn't hear nothing but owls after sundown," but there was music in the area. "The first time I ever heard a guitar played I thought it was a brass band coming through. I was a small kid and I asked my mother what was it and she said that was a guitar. I said, 'Ain't you going to get me one of those when I get large enough?' She said, 'Yeah, I'll get you one.' First thing I learned to play was an old banjo you understand, I say old banjo because I learned how to play that. I was just going up and down, plunk a lunk, plunk a lunk, plunk a lunk, I thought I was doing something playing that banjo..." In 1910 there was his first blues. "The first song that was a blues I heard was a man in a carnival singing 'I'm on the road somewhere, if the train don't break down I'm on the road somewhere!' ...then *Memphis Blues* and *Florida Blues* and *Hesitating Blues* and some girl blues, kind of imitate to her feeling. This come to be very famous..."

A sketch of Gary's life doesn't seem to have a strong relationship to his art. From his early recordings it is obvious that he was completely shaped as a musician by the time he was a young man. Except for his blindness whatever has happened to him has been only an incident, not an influence. He insists "...I only can sing what God tells me to sing..." and his music has its own strength and vitality. Even twenty years of singing on New York's streets left little mark on him. His voice roughened, but he still played his songs in the same style that he'd developed twenty years earlier, and he still feels the excitement of his music. Often the older bluesmen seem to be sitting uncomfortably with their new guitars looking down at their hands in silence while they try to remember their younger hungers and desires but with Gary there has been a continued renewal. "This is the music that God gave me to sing, and all I can do is try to make my way with it..."

With the passing of the years the only changes in Gary's art have been to make his music even more accessible. His religious songs, the great arrangements of *If I Had My Way (Samson and Delilah), Twelve Gates To The City, Death Don't Have No Mercy* and *You Got To Move* still have their fierce strength but the singing is even more expressive, there is an even richer sensed reality. Also he'll now sometimes perform his blues pieces in public, the *Candyman* that has been played and sung by dozens of his New York guitar students, and the minstrel song *She Wouldn't Say Quit*. Sometimes, too, he just sits back in his chair and plays the guitar. Only a handful of guitarists have the skill and vividness of his smaller pieces like *Buck Dance* or the sustained interest of his longer improvisations, *Twelve Sticks*. Just as a river flows with renewed strength as it nears its mouth, Gary's music has become an even more vital current in his late years.*

*This article was written in 1968.

Devil's Dream

Key: F
Section transcribed: The first section as well as bridge.
Source: Pure Religion and Bad Company—77 Records

The key of F has never been a favorite for bluesmen, ragtime guitarists or songsters. Rev. Davis, however, perfected several styles in this key. One is the eerie guitar sound of the religious numbers, *Blow Gabriel, God's Gonna Separate, Decided To Go Down* and *The Angel's Message To Me.* This we will study in the next volume of Rev. Davis' guitar techniques. Another way of playing in the key of F was the manner he used in *Come Down To See Me Sometime.* This gives the impression of minstrel picking and is a very difficult style to transcribe or teach. The third approach was to use an alternating bass. This is the method used in *Devil's Dream.*

The first challenge will be to finger the F chord as Rev. Davis did. This is in fact, the way most folk and blues players play this chord position. (Classical guitarists bar all six strings with the index finger and then form the chord. This however, leaves them at a disadvantage as a tune like *Devil's Dream* could never be played around this positioning.)

There is a basic theme as indicated in the transcribed first section. This is played with an alternating bass. The bridge is a rhythmic picking pattern on a Dm and A⁷ chord followed by the guitar imitating the sound of the devil snoring!

This type of tune is what I call a show instrumental. I have included it in this volume so that we could study the key of F. A more complex show instrumental of Rev. Davis' is his famous *Soldiers' Drill* (also played in the key of F) which will be transcribed in the next Rev. Davis volume.

Devil's Dream

Traditional. Arranged and adapted by Rev. Gary Davis

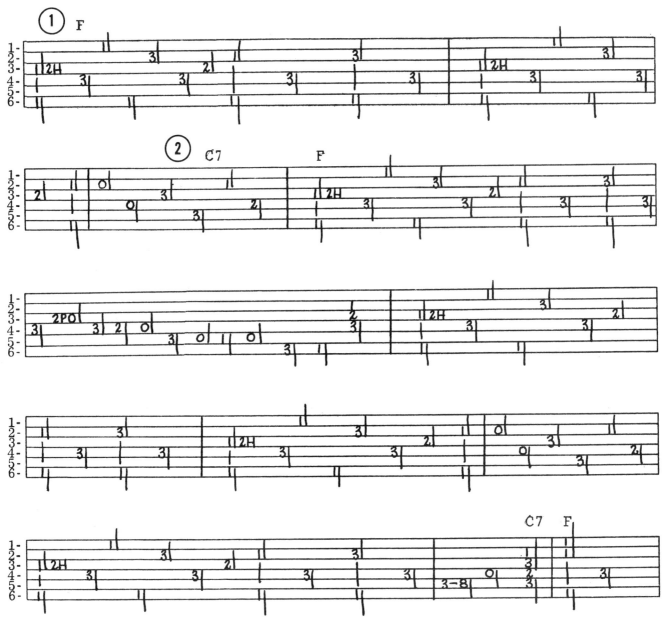

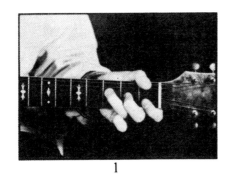

1

2

Bridge:

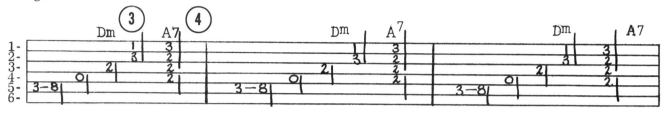

SLIDE ON 5th STRING TO IMITATE
A SNORING SOUND

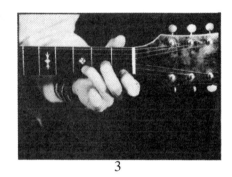

3

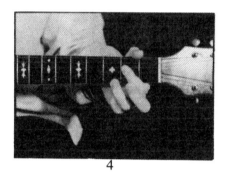

4

Devil's Dream

Cross And Evil Woman Blues

Key: E
Section transcribed: The guitar introduction and first verse.
Source: Rev. Gary Davis 1935-1949—Yazoo Records

This is a difficult blues in the key of E. It has many of Rev. Davis' trademarks. The same approach is also used in his religious song *Sun Is Goin' Down*.

The guitar introduction is reminiscent of the old 78's of Lonnie Johnson (a guitarist that Rev. Davis admired). The most difficult aspect of this arrangement is the playing of it to the proper speed.

There is an interesting texture change when the introduction goes into the guitar accompaniment behind the first verse. In the verse section the guitar gently flows underneath the words highlighting phrases by using rhythmic variations, and bass runs.

In his latter years Rev. Davis always refused to sing this song. He would perform it as an instrumental calling it *Ice Pick Blues*.

Guitar Introduction:

Words and music by Rev. Gary Davis

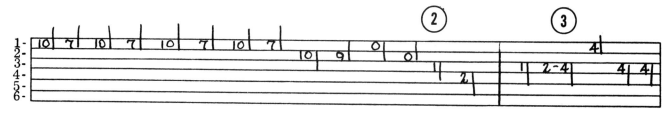

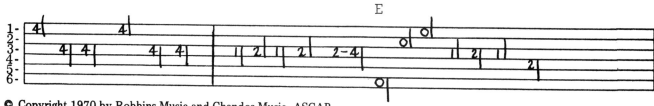

Cross And Evil Woman Blues

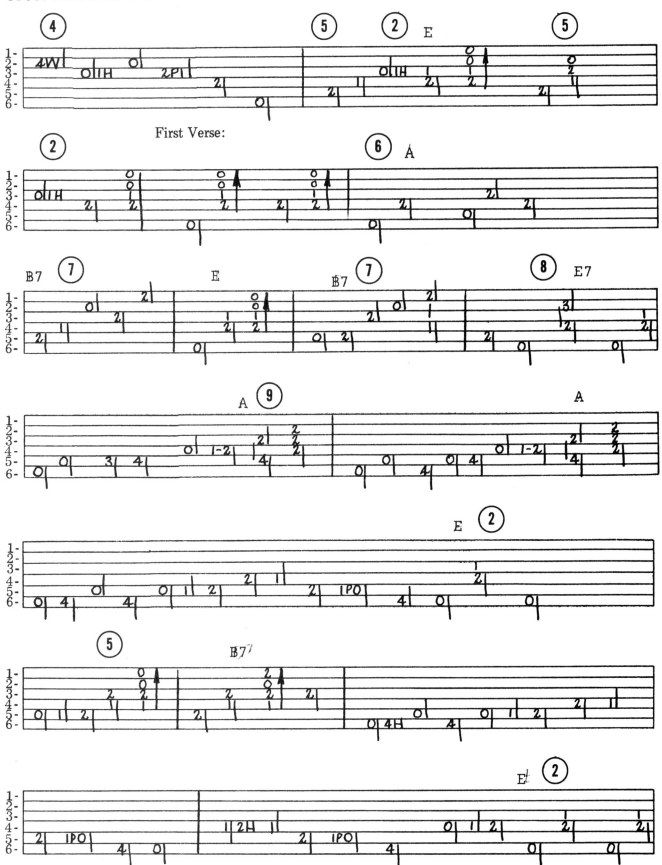

1

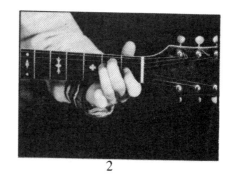

2

3

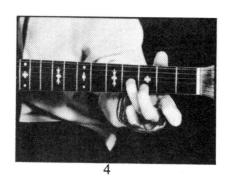

4

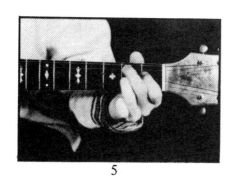

5

6

7

8

9

Cross And Evil Woman Blues

Lord, ___ you wom-en ___ sure do treat me ___ mean.

Lord, ___ you wom-en sure do treat me mean.

Why, you treat me just like I was ___

some man ___ has nev-er been seen.

When you find a woman wake up in the morning with a rag tied around her head (2X)
She got an evil mind, kill some poor man dead

She get up cross and evil and she can't hardly be pleased (2X)
Nothing you can do to please that woman if you get on down on your bending knees

Don't a woman feel good and satisfied when she knows she got a man alone (2X)
'Cause she feel hot and evil when she knows a no good woman is helping him along

You get a jealous hearted woman, she's a kind of woman that's hard to quit (2X)
If you ever get one on your hands, sure God never quit

Lord, when a jealous hearted woman start to loving get crazy, get out of her mind (2X)
All she wants is a shotgun or razor, ice-pick or pistol she can find

First verse:

I'm Throwin' Up My Hands

Key: A
Section transcribed: The guitar introduction and first verse.
Source: Rev. Gary Davis—1935-1949—Yazoo Records

This is one of the classic and most influential guitar arrangements to come out of the thirties. It is this guitar part that Blind Boy Fuller, Brownie McGee and many other bluesmen used on hundreds of blues recordings.

I have transcribed the introduction and first verse. This as *Cross And Evil Woman Blues* shows an interesting texture change between the guitar breaks and sung verses. During the guitar solos the melody is taken up the neck. (In some ways this reminds me of Blind Lemon Jefferson's *Black Snake Moan.*) During the verses the guitar flows underneath the words offering bass runs and rhythmic licks.

The eighth line of tab, as the guitar introduction is ending, shows a very involved end tag run. Here the chords quickly change from a D^7 to F to E^7. On top of this a short counter-point line is played. This is simplified at the end of the first verse. The speed that Rev. Davis played this on his 1935 recording is incredible and should take you some time to master.

Rev. Davis extended this approach into his religious arrangements, i.e. *Twelve Gates To The City* and *Meet You At The Station.* An interesting point to note for this blues as well as *Cross and Evil Woman Blues* is the vocal style used. For these blues Rev. Davis practically recites the words. When using the same type of arrangement to his gospel songs he puts much more emotion and energy into the vocal delivery.

Rev. Davis never sung this song in his later life. Instead it was presented as an instrumental called *Mountain Jack Blues.* He would also use the basic structure of the tune for having the guitar "talk." This can be heard on the *Lo' I Be With You Always* l.p. and the track entitled *Please Judy.*

Guitar Introduction:

Words and music by Rev. Gary Davis

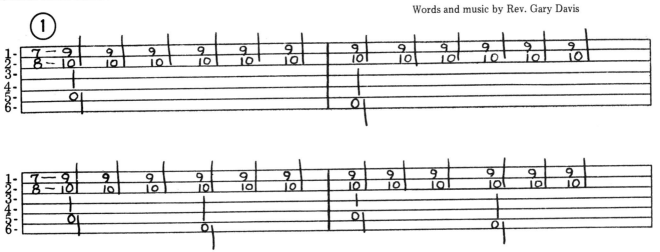

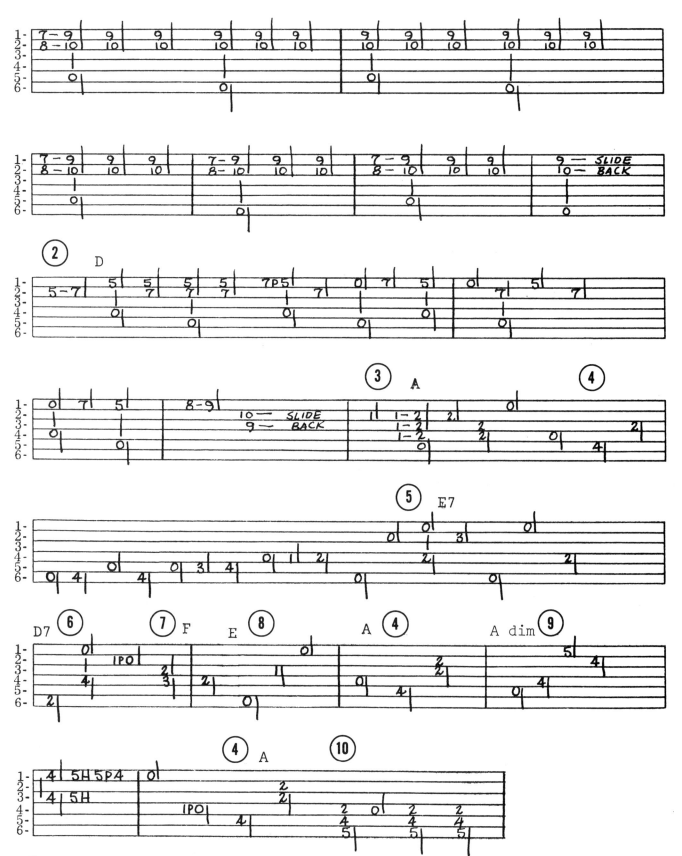

I'm Throwin' Up My Hands

First Verse:

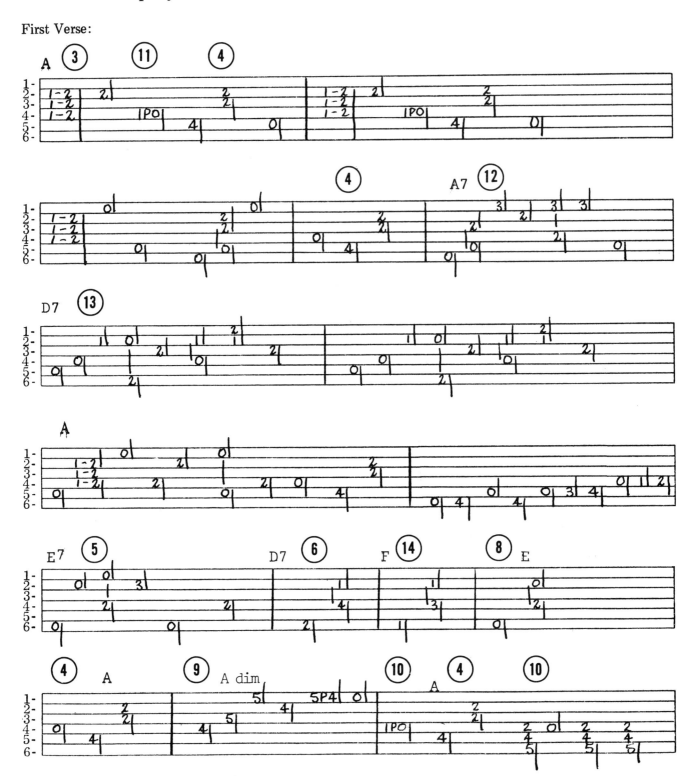

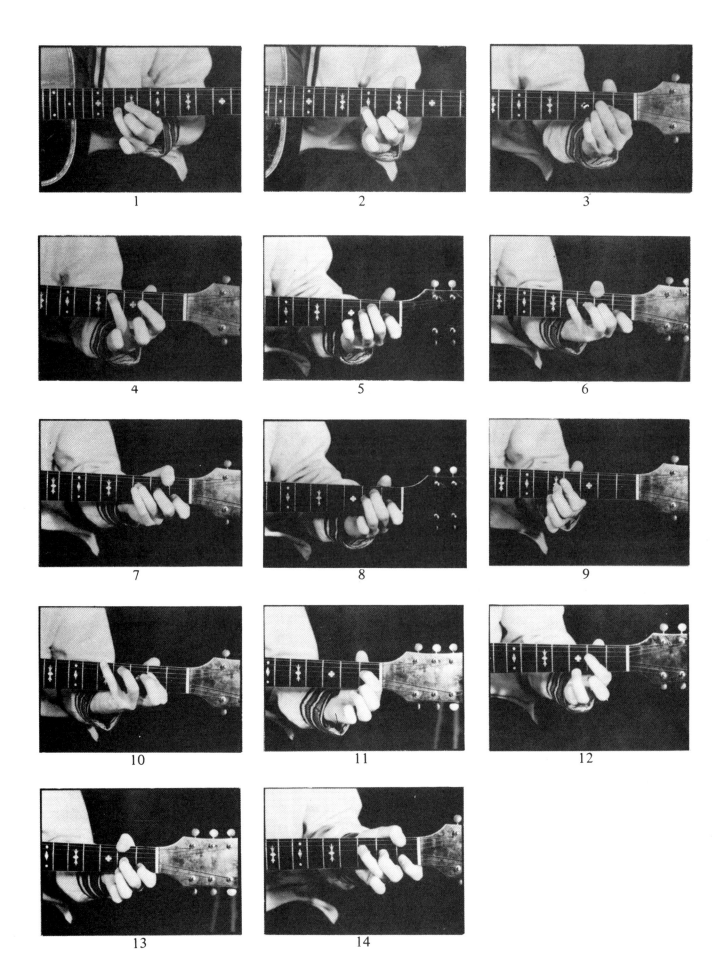

I'm Throwin' Up My Hands

If I could hol - ler___ just like a moun - tain - jack,___

A   **D7**

if I could hol - ler___ just like a moun - tain - jack,___

A   **E7**

___ I'd go up on the moun - tain,___

D7   **E7**   **A**   **D#** **E7** **A**

hol - ler my ba - by___ back.___

There is one thing, sure do worry me (2x)
My good gal packed her suitcase,
    walked off and left poor me

Lord, Lord, see what a fix she left me in (2x)
I ain't got no home, and ain't got no friends

I'm going away to wear you off my mind (2x)
Said I won't be here wringing my hands and crying

Guitar introduction:

First verse:

Death Don't Have No Mercy

Key: G

Section transcribed: Accompaniment for first verse with several variations and
the guitar break.

Source: When I Die I'll Live Again—Fantasy Records

> *Harlem Street Singer*—Prestige Bluesville
> *Let Us Get Together*—Kicking Mule Records

This is one of the most popular of Rev. Davis' *Holy Blues.* I have included it in
this volume as it can serve as a bridge between Rev. Davis' blues guitar styles and
the techniques and styles he used for arranging and playing his religious numbers.

Death Don't Have No Mercy is a beautiful, haunting piece of music. The
guitar accompaniment is comparatively simple. Basically, it is just a chord progression being strummed with occassional bass runs. I have indicated two variations of the bass runs played around the Em section.

The guitar break takes the melody up the neck using several difficult chord
positions but essentially composed around the melody being picked on the treble
strings. It was this section that Rev. Davis would say, "Talk to me Miss Gibson."

A very interesting version of this tune has been recorded by the group Hot
Tuna.

The term "Holy Blues" was created to try and describe a style of Rev.
Davis'. For these songs the spirit of "blues playing" is evident yet the message is
religious.

Accompaniment for Verses:

Words and music by Rev. Gary Davis

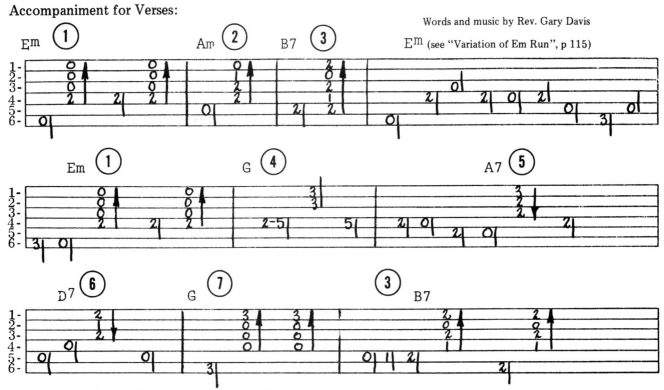

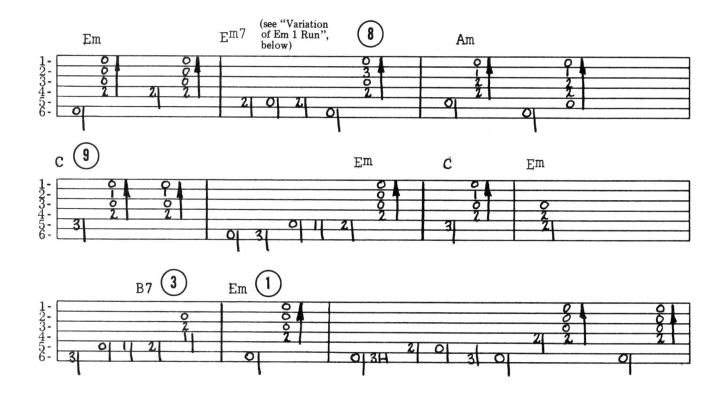

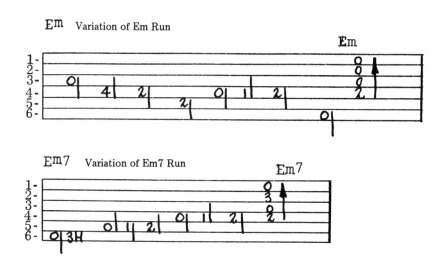

(see "Guitar Break," p.116)

Death Don't Have No Mercy

Guitar Break:

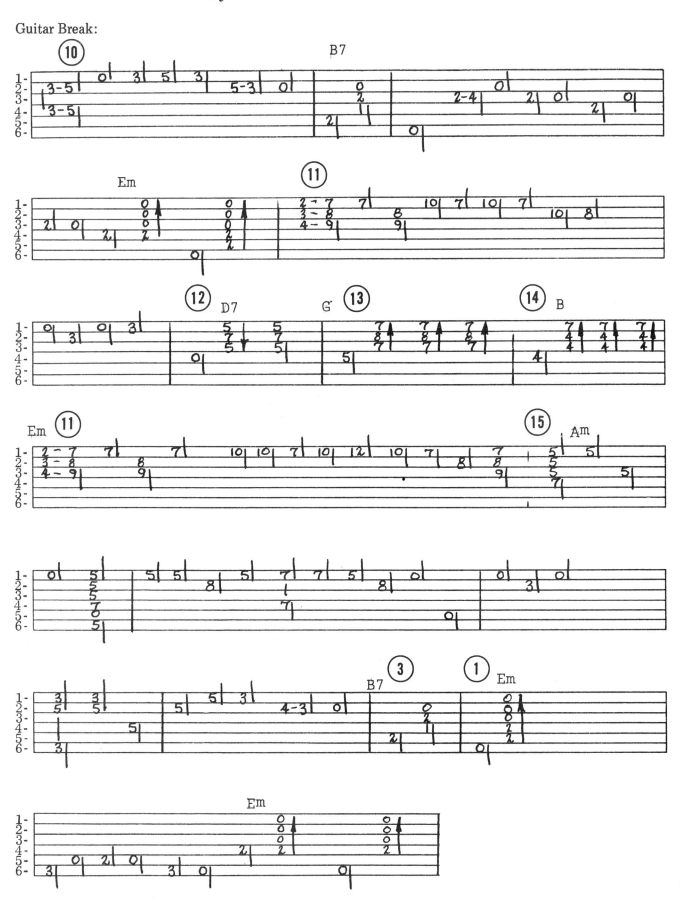

116

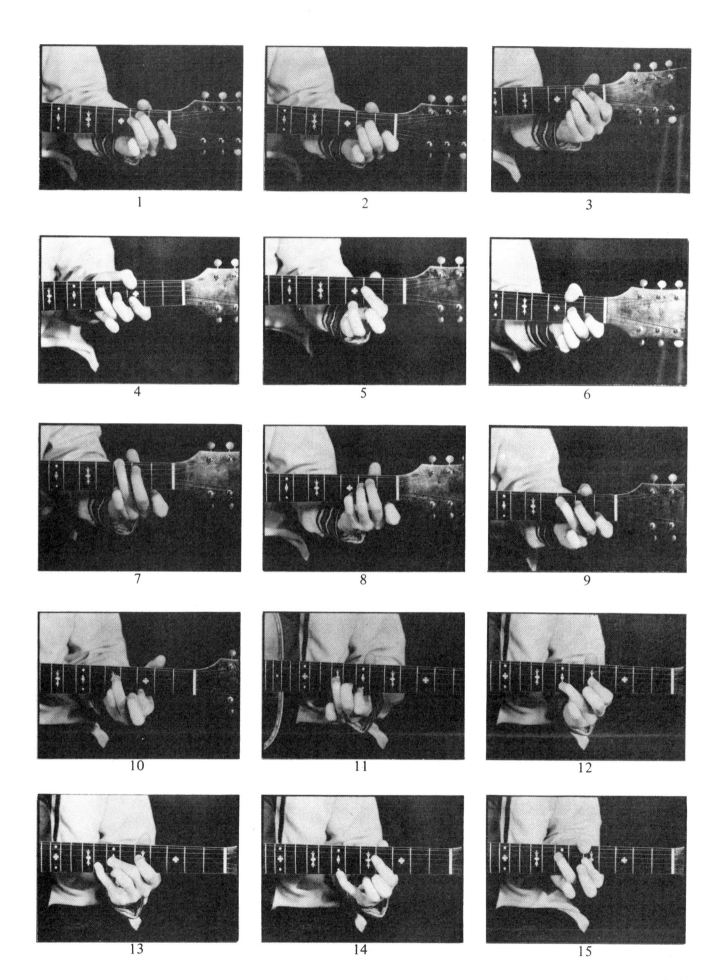

Death Don't Have No Mercy

Well death will go in any family in this land (2x)
Well it come to your house and it won't stay long
Well you look in the bed and one of the family
   be gone
Well death will go in any family in this land

Well he never takes a vacation in this land (2x)
Well he come to your house and he won't stay long
You look in the bed and your mother will be gone
Death never takes a vacation in this land

Well he'll leave you standing and crying in this land (2x)
It come to your house and won't stay long
You look in the bed and somebody be gone
Well he'll leave you standing and crying in this land

Oh death always in a hurry in this land (2x)
Well he come to your house and he won't stay long
You look in the bed and your mother will be gone
Oh death always in a hurry in this land

He won't give you time to get ready in this land (2x)
It come to your house and won't stay long
You look in the bed and somebody be gone
He won't give you time to get ready in this land

Accompaniment for verse:

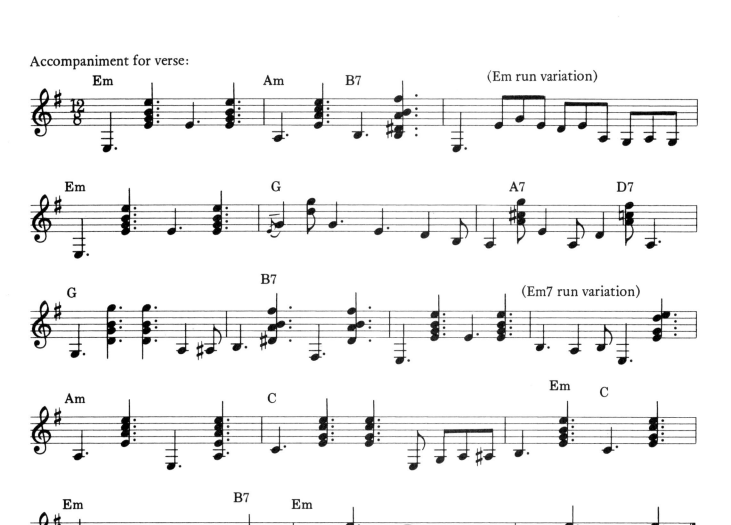

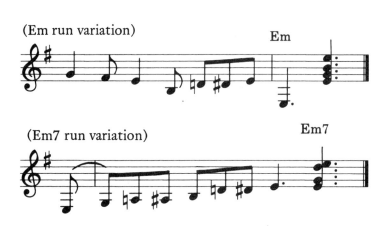

Death Don't Have No Mercy

Guitar break:

You be too perfect then the mistakes been already made. But you go try to do a thing and make a mistake to start off with, then that's the best start in life. It gives somebody a chance to correct you."

Whistlin' Blues

Key: The guitar is in an open tuning—D A D F♯ A B
Section transcribed: The part where Rev. Davis tells how the piano played.
Source: Blues and Gospel—Biograph Records

Our study of the blues guitar techniques of Rev. Davis is just about finished. There is a lot of material in this book. I think, enough to keep you busily occupied for several months if not years. The last selection I would like to present is a very unique bottleneck tune. This is an instrumental with a story (similar to *Lost Boy In The Wilderness*).

The first unusual aspect of this arrangement is the tuning that the guitar is placed. Here the strings are tuned D A D F♯ A B. This is quite unique and I have never discovered another old tune that used this tuning. (This was a typical Rev. Davis surprise. He was disdainful of bottleneck playing and open chord tunings. So when the opportunity came to show me such a piece wouldn't you guess that he'd pick an unusual tuning and a beautiful melody!)

Over the fourth or last finger of your left hand you should place a bottleneck. This implies exactly what it is—a neck of a bottle. If for some reason there are no broken bottles around your home a metal tube, a metal lipstick holder or a glass cigar holder will do. You then gently fret the strings and frets indicated though making sure the strings are not pressed down. The desired effect is a sliding whining one, similar to the Hawaiian guitar sounds in old Bing Crosby movies. The difficult technique is to gain control of the sliding sound and this will make the difference between a blues sound and an Hawaiian one.

This style can be studied much further and you can find a discussion of several classic bottleneck arrangements in the book Delta Blues Guitar (Oak).

I have recorded a version of this tune on my *How To Play Blues Guitar* l.p. Here it is treated as a guitar instrumental and I vary verse to verse using different rhythmic right hand licks that Rev. Davis taught me.

To re-tune the guitar I generally first tune the guitar to a Vestapol tuning (D A D F♯ A D) and then lower the first string to a B. Here are some hints how you can easily do this operation:

I am presuming that we are starting from standard tuning. Thus our guitar would be tuned: E A D G B E. We must first change this to: D A D F♯ A D. You will notice that the fifth and fourth strings remain constant.

There are two methods used to re-tune the guitar. One is by ear and the other by fretting various positions on various strings to hear the proper tones. Let us discuss the first method:

1. Since the fourth string will stay at D we can then use this as a guide. We lower the sixth string until it sounds identical to the fourth string an octave lower.

We can now lower the first string, the high E, to a D note or until it also sounds like the fourth string but this time an octave higher. We now re-tune the second string by bringing it down until it sounds identical to the fifth string with the difference being that it too sounds an octave higher. The third string offers the only problem. Try bringing this string down until the note sounds correct. You can check this by playing and listening to the whole chord. It should sound like a D chord. To check the third string you need only fret the fourth fret of the fourth string and this will give you the proper pitch. This last step will take a little trial and error.

Whistlin' Blues

2. The second method is a little longer but perhaps safer. We re-tune the sixth string using the same procedure as in the dropped D tuning. The third string is re-tuned by using the method explained in #1. We then fret the third fret of the third string and this gives us the proper note for the second string. Once we have lowered the second string to its position we fret the fifth fret of this string and this gives us the proper note for the first string.

Now the first string must be re-tuned to B. This can be done by playing the second fret of the second string which gives us the proper note to bring this string down to. To check the full open chord, fret the third fret of the first string and strum all six strings. This will sound identical to the open D chord (Vestapol).

Words and music by Rev. Gary Davis

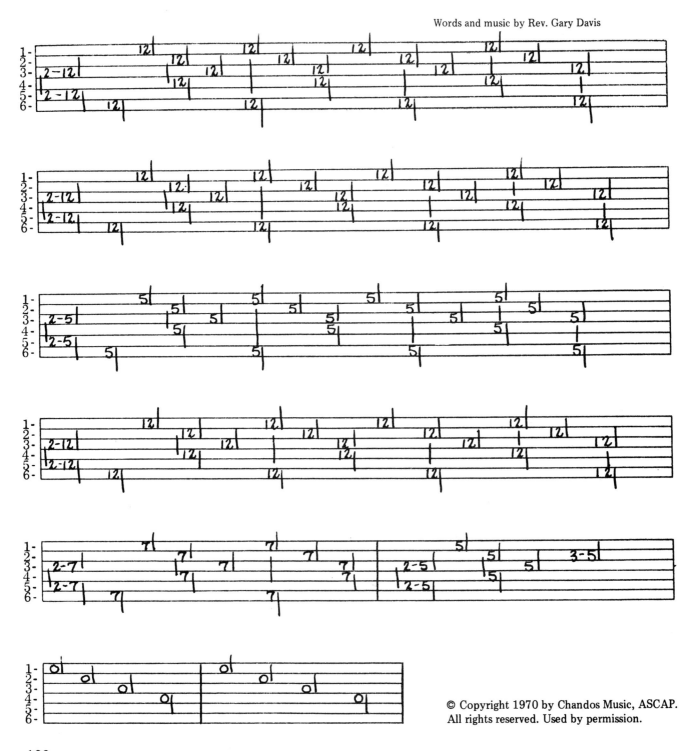

note:
this is the story recited against a simple guitar
lick as indicated in the last line of tab.

Now there's a little talk going to come behind this, you know

I was walking downtown in a place I had never been before
All dressed up and I didn't have no money
I didn't think about it, you understand, 'til the sun begin to start to bend low
I always dressed up fancy, to feel good and stuff like that
Something told me to look up at the sun and see how high the sun was
I saw the sun bending low and it struck my mind 'bout where I was going to spend the night at
I was beginning to get worried 'bout it, you know
Beginnin' to get serious
I looked up the street and I saw a woman, you know
She was coming down the street
She looked so good
She had hair like Mary and walked just like the Lord
I begin to walk kind of pretty, you know, to herself, you know
She met a man before she got to me but she whistled at me like this:
    (whistle)
That's right, you know

She just walking through pretty, you know, after a while she met this man but she still kept her eyes on me
So, I couldn't wait, you know, and the sun was going down
I wanted to find somewhere where to locate myself, you know
She whistled at me again
Like this:
    (whistle)
I stopped then, you know
She got up with me, you know and she threw her arms around me and kiss me
Said, "Come on let's go to a dance tonight"

You know how young people is
They don't think about getting hurt or nothing like that kind no more
She was first talking to me about how she didn't have nobody, you know
She said, "Let's stop by the liquor store"
Stopped by there and got a pint of 'Rock And Rye' you know,
    and cut it in half and told me to take the other half
She come around me and told me to come around to this house where they were having a piano dance
She sit me right down on a stool, right beside her you know,
    and she become to playing this thing called the Whistlin' Blues
How you reckon she done that Listen:

(Here Rev. Davis played the transcribed section presented.)

Whistlin' Blues

Final Discussion

Rev. Davis had a unique way of holding and playing his guitar. How he held his instrument can be seen in several of the photographs of him presented in this book.

During his youth Rev. Davis broke his left wrist (the story of this incident is recounted in the interview) and it set in an unusual position. The hand was set somewhat to the left of the axis of the arm. This allowed him to play many unorthodox and difficult chord positions. These might prove challenging to you but practice and developing the left hand muscles will enable you to play these chords. (These are played in *Baby, Let Me Follow You Down, Cross and Evil Woman Blues, I'm Throwin' Up My Hands* and several other numbers. These positions will be more dominant in the next Rev. Davis volume.)

Rev. Davis' right hand picking technique is based on the use of only the thumb and index finger. In general, he used a thumb-pick and a plastic finger-pick. However, for certain numbers he preferred to play with his bare fingertips. Usually, *Cocaine Blues, Saddle It Around, Candyman* and *Spoonful* were played in this manner. The result was a much "softer" sound. The use of finger-picks usually depended on how tired his hands were. If very tired then he would use the picks to enable him to play louder and "save his fingers."

There are no rules for the way in which Rev. Davis used his thumb and index fingers. Many times the thumb would play treble notes in order to give them the right accenting. (Naturally a note hit with the thumb would be more heavily accented than the same note played with the index finger.)

When playing single string runs Rev. Davis would generally alternate every other note between his thumb and index fingers. The tablature system clearly indicates which finger is to play which note.

Rev. Davis also developed "rolls" or "rhythmic licks." These generally double time the existing meter. These are achieved by allowing the thumb to play a roll against the index finger playing the dominant note in that key. This sound is slightly touched upon in several songs in this volume but will be explored in more detail when we study the rags and show instrumentals in the next book.

Rev. Davis rarely used open tunings. The only exception has been included in this study, i.e. *Whistlin' Blues*. He never used a capo and was quite proud of this fact that enabled him to perfect his playing in every key.

I suggest you also see my other Oak guitar instruction books as these will help to develop your techniques. Especially of interest in relationship to Rev. Davis' guitar styles is the volume Ragtime Blues Guitarists. This studies various techniques of Blind Blake, Big Bill Broonzy, Blind Lemon Jefferson and Blind Boy Fuller.

More later
Peace

Stefan Grossman

Discography

Since 1960 there have been 16 solo l.p.'s released featuring Rev. Gary Davis. What is most amazing upon listening to all of these discs is that each holds an exciting and unique musical experience. Some feature his religious songs. Others his ragtime guitar instrumentals. There are a few live recorded in concert l.p.'s, and three albums showing how Rev. Davis used to play in the ambient of his home. There is even a valuable re-issue album that brings most of Rev. Davis' rare old 78's on one l.p.

I have a clear preference amongst these albums for six that I feel have captured the essence of Rev. Davis' spirit, whether playing rags, gospel or blues tunes. These are:

When I Die I'll Live Again
Fantasy 24704

This is a double album that brings together the first two Prestige Bluesville albums that Rev. Davis recorded. The original titles were *Blind Gary Davis / Harlem Street Singer* and *A Little More Faith*. These were recorded at Rudy Van Gelder's studio in New Jersey and the sessions were produced by Ken Goldstein. The performances and sound quality for both albums are excellent. These two discs feature the most exciting religious numbers in Rev. Davis' repertoire.

Reverend Gary Davis 1935-1949
Yazoo L-1023

This is a re-issue album of Rev. Davis' ARC 78's and two songs he recorded in 1949 for the Lenox label in New York City. Among the 14 selections are the two blues Rev. Davis recorded in 1935. These two tunes are both transcribed in this book and it is interesting to hear the difference in approach between these two numbers and the religious songs. Several of the gospel tunes can also be found on the Fantasy l.p. (described above); note that the arrangements stayed the same over a thirty year period. This is an important album in order to gain a perspective about Rev. Davis' guitar playing and singing techniques. The sound quality is also surprisingly good for a re-issue album. One of the most fascinating songs on the album is a tune in the key of F called *The Angels Message To Me*. When I asked Rev. Davis to play this tune in the early sixties he could not remember the music, title or words. He was very pleased and surprised when I brought to him a tape of his old recording of the tune.

Gospel, Blues And Street Songs
Riverside RLP 148

This album might be difficult to find. It first appeared in the early sixties and several times since has re-appeared. One side features the songs and playing of Pink Anderson while the second side is devoted to Rev. Davis. The performances on this record are very moving. There are eight songs including three that were also recorded during the 1935 ARC sessions. *There Was A Time That I Was Blind* and *Blow Gabriel* are highlights in this collection.

Ragtime Guitar
Transatlantic Records TRA 244 (in Europe)
Kicking Mule Records (in the States)

This is a collection of ten ragtime guitar instrumentals. I produced this album as well as the next two. My approach in making an album of Rev. Davis was to collect hours and hours of tapes of Rev. Davis playing all types of music in all kinds of environments and circumstances. My tape collection has hours of material recorded at Rev. Davis' home, in church and in concert. From these performances I would choose the best version of any particular tune I wanted to see on an l.p. In this way I could pick from six to ten versions of one song in order to get the best "take." I believe this is the best method for producing any artist but of course it is very time consuming and an ordinary record company could not go about making records in this manner. However, I have used this method for four l.p.'s of Rev. Davis and I believe the results speak for themselves.

Ragtime Guitar shows the guitar genius of Rev. Davis. Many of these tunes will be transcribed in my next book on Rev. Davis' rags and show tunes.

Children Of Zion
Transatlantic Records TRA 249 (in Europe)
Kicking Mule Records (in the States)

This is a live concert album recorded in the early sixties in Cambridge, Mass. It features a well rounded program of material ranging from gospel to rags, to show tunes to—would you believe—*Long Way To Tipperary!*

This l.p. captures the excitment of a Rev. Davis performance and is essential for your collection.

Lo' I Be With You Always
Kicking Mule Records

This is a double album. The first two sides are a concert performance at Michigan State recorded in 1969. What was surprising in this concert was that Rev. Davis preferred to play his blues over his gospel songs. There are long versions of *Hesitation Blues, Baby, Let Me Lay It On You* and *She's Funny That Way* (all transcribed in this book). On side three there are three selections taken from two different concerts. The first is a definitive version of *Candyman* recorded in 1963 at Gerdes Folk City (a small folk-bar-club in New York City).

The second and third selections on this side were recorded at the Mariposa Folk Festival in 1959. Here Rev. Davis is joined by the Georgia Sea Island Singers. It is a very moving experience as Rev. Davis gets the "spirit" and is able to communicate this to an outdoor audience of 10,000 people. Side four is a cross-section of material recorded at Rev. Davis' home in 1962. It features a beautiful blues instrumental—*Whoopin' Blues* as well as Rev. Davis playing the part of an accompanist to a girl singer named Suzy. This is one of my favorite Rev. Davis collections as it shows so many sides of his playing, techniques and styles.

I think these six albums will show you the spirit, music and feelings of Rev. Gary Davis. They also feature an incredible amount of excellent guitar playing. In fact, so much that it overwhelms me.

There are other albums that are available. Some of these can be easily found while others might be difficult. Here is a listing of these:

Blind Gary Davis—The Singing Reverend—*Stinson SLP* 56
Pure Religion And Bad Company—*77 Records* 77LA 12/14
Say No To The Devil—*Prestige Bluesville* 1049
The Guitar And Banjo Of Rev. Gary Davis—*Prestige Folklore* 14033
The Rev. Gary Davis At Newport—*Vanguard Everyman Classics SRV* 73008
Bring Your Money, Honey—*Fontana SFJL* 914
Blues And Gospel—*Biograph 12034*
New Blues And Gospel—*Biograph 12030*
Let Us Get Together—*Kicking Mule Records*

A tape has been prepared that features all the material presented in this book. Information regarding this can be obtained by writing:

Black Patty Tape Service
c/o Grossman
32 Gramercy Park South, Apt. 14a,
New York, New York 10003

Some addresses that may be helpful to you in locating the records listed (as well as other blues and ragtime albums) are:

Transatlantic Records
86 Marylebone High Street
London W.1
England

Yazoo Records
245 Waverly Place
New York City, N.Y.
10012

77 Records
77 Charing Cross Road
London W.C.2
England

Biograph Records
P.O. Box 109
Canaan, N.Y.
12129

Kicking Mule Records
P.O. Box 3233
Berkeley, California
94703

European records, such as Transatlantic or 77 Records can be ordered from:
Collet's Record Shop
70 New Oxford Street
London
England

Below is a listing of the songs featured in this book and from what source they were taken:
Saddle It Around, Black Patty Tape Service
Cocaine Blues, Let Us Get Together / Kicking Mule Records
Coco Blues, Pure Religion And Bad Company / 77 Records
You Got The Pocket Book..., Black Patty Tape Service
Lost Boy In The Wilderness, Say No To The Devil / Prestige Bluesville 1049
Candyman, Lo' I Be With You Always / Kicking Mule Records
Two Step Candyman, Ragtime Guitar / Transatlantic Records 244, Kicking Mule Records
Goin' To Chattanooga, Black Patty Tape Service
Spoonful, The Rev. Gary Davis At Newport / Vanguard Everyman Classics—SRV 73008
Mine All Troubled Blues, Black Patty Tape Service
Baby, Let Me Lay It On You, Lo' I Be With You Always / Kicking Mule Records
She's Funny That Way, Lo' I Be With You Always / Kicking Mule Records,
Blues and Gospel—Biograph 12030
Save Up Your Money..., Black Patty Tape Service
Sally, Where'd You Get Your Liquor From, Blues And Gospel / Biograph 12030,
Black Patty Tape Service
Hesitation Blues, Lo' I Be With You Always / Kicking Mule Records
Walkin' Dog Blues, Ragtime Guitar / Transatlantic Records 244, Kicking Mule Records
Devil's Dream, Pure Religion And Bad Company / 77 Records
Cross And Evil Woman Blues, Rev. Gary Davis 1935-1949 / Yazoo Records L-1023
I'm Throwin' Up My Hands, Rev. Gary Davis 1935-1949 / Yazoo Records L-1023
Death Don't Have No Mercy, When I Die I'll Live Again / Fantasy 24704
Harlem Street Singer / Prestige Bluesville 1015
Let Us Get Together / Kicking Mule Records
Whistlin' Blues, Blues And Gospel / Biograph 22030
Below is a listing of the records of Rev. Davis with the selections that appear on each album:

When I Die I'll Live Again
Fantasy 24704
Samson and Delilah
Let Us Get Together
    Right Down Here
I Belong To The Band
Pure Religion
Great Change Since I Been Born
Death Don't Have No Mercy
Twelve Gates To The City
Goin' To Sit Down On The Banks Of The
    River
Tryin' To Get Home
Lo' I Be With You Always
I Am The Light Of This World
Lord, I Feel Just Like Goin' On
You Got To Move
Crucifixion
I'm Glad I'm In That Number
There's A Table Sittin' In Heaven
Motherless Children
There's A Bright Side Somewhere
I'll Be All Right Some Day
You Better Mind
A Little More Faith
I'll Fly Away
God's Gonna Separate
When I Die I'll Live Again
Lo' I Be With You Always
Kicking Mule Records
She's Funny That Way
Baby, Let Me Lay It On You
Please Judy
The Boy Was Kissing The Girl...
Hesitation Blues
Candyman
I Got Religion, I'm So Glad
I'm A Soldier In The Army Of The Lord
Children Of Zion
Whoopin' Blues
What Could I Do
Lo' I Be With You Always
Blind Gary Davis—The Singing
    Reverend
Stinson SLP56
Death Is Riding Everyday (Sun is Goin'
    Down)
Jesus Met The Woman At The Well
Oh, What A Beautiful City (Twelve Gates
    To The City)
Say No To The Devil
Motherless Children
Bad Company Brought Me Here
I Can't Make the Journey By Myself
You Got To Move
(On this album Rev. Davis is accompanied
by Sonny Terry on harmonica. The titles in
parentheses are the correct song titles.)
Pure Religion And Bad Company
77 Records 77LA 12/14
Pure Religion
Mountain Jack
Right Now
Buck Dance
Candyman
Devil's Dream
Moon Goin' Down
Coco Blues
Runnin' To The Judgement
Hesitation
Bad Company
I Didn't Want To Join The Band
Evening Sun Goes Down
Seven Sisters
My Heart is Fixed

Reverend Gary Davis 1935-1949
Yazoo L-1023
The Angel's Message To Me
The Great Change In Me
I'm Throwin' Up My Hands
You Got To Go Down
I Can't Bear My Burden By Myself
I Belong To The Band
I Am The True Vine
Lord, Stand By Me
Twelve Gates To The City
Have More Faith In Jesus
O Lord, Search My Heart
You Can Go Home
Meet Me At The Station
Cross And Evil Woman Blues
Gospel, Blues And Street Songs
Riverside RLP 148
Blow Gabriel
Twelve Gates To The City
Samson and Delilah
Oh Lord, Search My Heart
Get Right Church
You Got To Go Down
Keep Your Lamp Trimmed and Burning
There Was A Time That I Was Blind

Ragtime Guitar
Transatlantic Records 244 /
Kicking Mule Records
Cincinnatti Flow Rag
West Coast Blues
Buck Rag
St. Louis Tickle
Two Step Candyman
Walkin' Dog Blues
Italian Rag
C-Rag
Waltz Time Candyman
Make Believe Stunt
Children Of Zion
Transatlantic Records 249 /
Kicking Mule Records
I'm Going To Sit Down On The Banks Of
    The River
Twelve Gates To The City
(I heard the) Angels Singing
Twelve Sticks
Long Way To Tipperary
When The Train Comes Along (Meet You
    At The Station)
Come Down And See Me Sometime
Buck Dance
Soldiers' Drill
Say No To The Devil
Prestige Bluesville 1049
Say No To The Devil
Time Is Drawing Near
Hold To God's Unchanging Hand
Bad Company Brought Me Here
I Decided To Go Down
Lord, I Looked Down The Road
Little Bitty Baby
No One Can Do Me Like Jesus
Lost Boy In The Wilderness
Trying To Get To Heaven In Due Time
The Guitar And Banjo Of Reverend
    Gary Davis
Prestige Folklore 14033
Maple Leaf Rag (Make Believe Stunt)
Slow Drag (Cincinnati Flow Rag)
The Boy Was Kissing The Girl...
Candyman
United States March (Soldiers' Drill)
Devil's Dream

The Coon Hunt
Mister Jim (Walkin' Dog Blues)
Please Baby (Baby, Let Me Lay It On You)
Fast Fox Trot (Buck Rag)
Can't Be Satisfied (Mountain Jack Blues)
    (The titles in parentheses indicate the
    correct song titles.)
The Rev. Gary Davis At Newport
Vanguard Everyman Classics SRV
    73008
Samson and Delilah
I Won't Be Back No More
Buck Dance
Twelve sticks
Death Don't Have No Mercy
You Got To Move
Lovin' Spoonful (Spoonful)
She Wouldn't Say Quit
I've Done All My Singing For My Lord
Twelve Gates To The City
I Will Do My Last Singing In This Land
    Somewhere

Bring Your Money, Honey
Fontana SFJL 914
Twelve Gates To The City
Samson And Delilah
Keep Your Lamp Trimmed and Burning
The Boy Was Kissing The Girl...
Birmingham Special
Time Ain't So Long
Silvie
Lost John
Lo' I Be With You Always

Blues And Gospel
Biograph 12030
How Happy I Am
(I Heard The) Angels Singing
Samson and Delilah
Children of Zion
Soon My Work Will All Be Done
Talk On The Corner (She's Funny That
    Way)
Sally, Where'd You Get Your Liquor From
Hesitation Blues
Whistling Blues
Lost John

Lord I Wish I Could See
Biograph 12034
You Better Get Right (Sun Is Goin' Down)
Lord I Wish I Could See (There Was A
    Time When I Went Blind)
Be Mindful Of Your Sacrament
Down By The River (Goin' To Sit Down
    On The Banks Of The River)
Eagle Rocking Blues (Mine All Troubled
    Blues)
Candyman
Crow Jane
Cocaine Blues
I'll Do My Last Singing (In This Land
    Somewhere)
Let Us Get Together
Kicking Mule Records
Let Us Get Together
Death Don't Have No Mercy
Cocaine Blues
Your Goin' Quit Me Baby
Oh Glory, How Happy I Am
There's Destruction In That Land
Tired, My Soul Needs A'Restin'
Georgia Camp Meeting
Blues In A
Fox Chase